early

Movement
Skills

early

Movement Skills

Naomi Benari

Speechmark Publishing Ltd
Telford Road, Bicester, Oxon OX26 4LQ, UK

Please note that in this text 'she' is used to refer to the child for the sake of clarity alone.

Published by
Speechmark Publishing Ltd, Telford Road, Bicester, Oxon, OX26 4LQ, United Kingdom
www.speechmark.net

© Naomi Benari, 1999
Reprinted 2001, 2003, 2005

002-3668/Printed in the United Kingdom/1010

British Library Cataloguing in Publication Data
Benari, Naomi
   Early Movement Skills. – (Early Skills Series)
   1. Movement education 2. Motor learning
   I. Title
   152.3'34

ISBN 0 83688 378 8
(Previously published by Winslow Press Ltd under ISBN 0 86388 224 2)

EARLY MOVEMENT SKILLS
Contents

FOREWORD

It gives me great delight to write the foreword for this much needed publication. Having spent some years investigating the role of physical movement, particularly in relation to musical performance and understanding, I am aware of the complex nature of this field.

The healthy integration of mind and body is an important and obvious aspect of a human being's overall functioning. The difficulty lies in the comprehensive nature of the term 'movement' for movement is involved in everything, from the use of the smallest to the largest muscles and even to the hidden inner imitation of movement. It is not surprising, therefore, that there is a void in publications that focus practically on physical movement and its importance to children's general development.

Naomi Benari's excellent handbook addresses this void. She successfully combines the evidence of research with practical application. The result is a comprehensive, graded sequence of activities, always with rationale, expressed with superb clarity. The work benefits from the author's wide research and experience in the field of movement therapy. It is addressed to an extensive audience of carers, teachers, therapists and parents engaged in promoting and supporting their children's physical, intellectual, emotional and social development.

In addition to the wealth of exercises intended to stimulate and to initiate movement the author reminds us of the 'how' and the 'why' of children's behaviour, that is to say the natural behaviour that children exhibit and then presents a cornucopia of imaginative and exciting activities which relates to this and the interests which engage them. The section on addressing specific problems will be particularly welcomed.

Dorothy Taylor

ACKNOWLEDGEMENTS

Above all, I would like to thank the children of Northview School, with whom I worked during the time that I was writing this volume. While having fun with them, I learnt so much. I would also like to thank Alex and Sam, whose development from birth I have observed and learnt from as I played with them.

The ideas and writings of Veronica Sherborne have been a great inspiration to me, and I would particularly like to thank Walli Meier, whose guidance over several years has been much appreciated. I am grateful to her for looking over the manuscript, making many helpful suggestions, and reminding me of fundamentals and priorities.

Thanks are also due to David Eccles for the illustrations.

Naomi Benari

INTRODUCTION

WHO IS THIS MANUAL FOR?

This manual is intended for anyone working with young children. It can be used in the home, in therapy clinics and in schools, nurseries and playgroups, including those catering for children with special needs.

Chronological age is never specified, as the development of children varies widely. The activities described are graded, and it is therefore advisable to start at the beginning and to work through each section. The book begins with descriptions of simple activities for the carer to initiate. These gradually become more complex and increasingly involve the participation of the child. While each section addresses different aspects of ability, most activities affect several facets of development. These have been cross-referenced.

It is hoped that the movements and activities described will not only be used as they are, but will stimulate and encourage carers to develop their own ideas and their own way of working.

WHERE TO WORK

Whether at home or in a school or group, ensure that the area is warm and as free as possible from objects which could distract. Try to establish a rule that you are not to be interrupted. For activities which require body contact with the floor, the floor should be smooth and warm. Wood is often warmer than vinyl, but be careful that there is no danger of splinters.

HOW TO WORK

Movement is primarily a satisfying activity. Make sure that the child always enjoys the sessions, as it is through having fun without pressure that children can learn and have new experiences. Be sensitive to the child's needs, so that no activity is continued beyond the point where it ceases to be fun.

TOUCH

In his book *Touching*, Ashley Montagu (1978) writes that 'tactile stimulation has profound effects, both physiological and behavioural, upon the organism', and this is now widely accepted by most of those working with babies and young children. It is for this reason that many hospitals give advice to new mothers on touch and massage before they take their new baby home.

When activities involving touch are undertaken in a school or institution, it is advisable that more than one qualified adult is present, and that the parents have agreed to its use. This is to avoid even the slightest possibility of accusations of abuse.

Where physical contact with the child is involved, be sure that your hands are warm. Hold firmly to give confidence, but do not inhibit any movement which the child herself instigates. Above all, feel what her needs and desires are. When room temperature allows, remove as much of the child's clothing as possible. It is through feeling contact with you and the floor that she will acquire and increase her own body awareness.

BENEFITS OF MOVEMENT FOR YOUNG CHILDREN

Physical Development

Movement is a most important activity in the development of young children. It can strengthen muscles and help to develop co-ordination. It enhances body control and, by increasing body awareness, can help children to acquire physical skills.

Spatial Awareness

By moving through space, seeing objects from different angles and feeling them touch her body as she moves, a child learns experientially about that space, the relative sizes of objects in it, their textures, and their three-dimensional quality.

Cognitive Development

From the earliest stages, movement enhances cognitive development and stimulates brain activity. It is through the growing awareness of her own body that a baby learns about the world, about weight, shape, space and size.

Piaget's research on child development (Donaldson, 1987) suggests that movement precedes thinking. The left hemisphere of the brain is believed to be associated with thinking and reasoning, and the right hemisphere with movement and spatial awareness. Formal education tends to favour the left side of the brain, often to the detriment of the right side, which is just as important to the development of the growing child.

It is by using both sides of the brain, by speaking, reinforced by moving, that language and concepts, such as the relationship between one object and another in space, or activities which occur earlier or later than each other, can be enhanced. Action songs, with their repetition and use of rhythm and music, greatly aid the acquisition of language. The 'FunSong Method' is based on the belief that action songs are 'the starting point for acquiring new words and mastering language structures', and Dorothy Taylor (1976), in her introduction to *Learning With Traditional Rhymes* states that 'the early development of co-ordination is both valuable and important to a child's later development'. In the same way, counting songs help to develop numeracy.

Research with Down's Syndrome children by Cohen and Sekeles (1988) found that greater mental alertness was achieved by increasing the children's physical ability, and Rayner (1971) found that freedom in body movement is necessary for the growth of the imagination.

Control & Self Discipline

Research by Pisciotta (1980) suggests that 'control of one's body can mean the beginning of self-control in general'. As a child learns to control her body in movement and dance, that mastery can extend to other areas of life, and can result in increased self-discipline.

Relationships & Social Skills

It is through moving with others, feeling their weight and the effect of her own weight on them, that a child develops relationship and turn-taking skills, and learns to consider others (Sherborne, 1990). Visually impaired children in particular can benefit from moving and dancing with others, thus experiencing in their bodies the needs and wishes of another person.

Emotional Development

Movement has importance far beyond the physical and cognitive. Freud (1923) suggested that the first ego is a body ego, and in his book, *Human Development* (1971), Rayner states that bodily experiences are central to feelings. It is through awareness of the body that individuals become aware of themselves. This awareness leads to the growth of self-esteem as the child acquires skills. Rolling, sitting, crawling, standing and walking coincide with the development of the emotions: for example, the joy of sitting and looking around, the pride of walking. The emotions are also stimulated by moving in different ways, with different qualities of movement. For example, a strong movement will enhance feelings of self-assertion and confidence; gentle movement will engender feelings of caring.

Integration

Movement can help to integrate the body, mind and emotions, thus helping the development of an integrated, secure, whole person (Payne, 1992). It is through the pleasure experienced at the development of her abilities that a child acquires confidence and self-esteem, which is then experienced in other aspects of her life.

Through movement it is possible to relate to a child at her level, enabling communication even with those who are not yet talking. For all of these reasons, this book is concerned primarily with movement and the benefits that can accrue from it.

USE OF VOICE

Your voice is the simplest and easiest stimulus to use. It is also the most effective. Talk to the child throughout the movement session, commenting on what she is doing, encouraging and praising her. Use the tone of your voice to emphasize what she is doing. For example, when you want her to raise a limb, let your voice go up in pitch, and when you want her to lower a limb, lower the pitch. When you want her to speed up, speak faster, and when you want her to slow down, speak slowly. Raise the volume of your voice when you want to encourage a strong movement and speak quietly when you want to calm the child down.

The sound of your voice will help the child to execute the movement with the dynamics, strength and speed to match the sound. Words learnt together with movements will often be remembered faster than those used alone. For example, as you comment on the child going through, under, over or round an object or person, the words will be associated with the action and will have more meaning for the child.

This commentary often evolves into singing, and indeed song is a very powerful stimulus for young children's learning. Small children like and respond positively to rhythm and song, and suggestions are made below, where appropriate, on the use of language and song. Most of the action songs included in this book have been chosen because they involve the whole body. Some songs are designed to help increase fine motor control and examples of these can be found in Section 2.

Use action songs (see Appendix I) when appropriate, and make up your own songs when you do not know of a relevant one. You may want to make up your own melodies, but if you do not have the confidence to do this you can use familiar tunes, adding words suitable to the movement activity you are engaged in.

MUSIC

The use of music will often encourage a reluctant or shy child to move and dance where voice alone may not do so. In addition, when music is chosen for its dynamic and emotional content, it can influence the quality of a movement and the feelings of the dancer. For more on music and rhythm, see Section 6.

Early Movement Skills

PICTURES & PHOTOGRAPHS

The showing of pictures can often be more effective than the simple use of verbal language, particularly for children who do not yet understand everything that is said to them, or who have not yet seen the object or had the experience that you are trying to communicate. In any case, for all children, pictures are more concrete. For example, the picture of a cat will convey immediately the fact that they walk on all fours, and the picture of a tree will communicate the fact of its breadth in relation to its height.

VIDEOS

These are often more effective than pictures when encouraging movement. While a picture can show the shape of an animal or object, it cannot give any idea of its size relative to the child, nor can it show how it moves.

Videos can also be used to tell short mimed or danced stories or rhymes. This gives the opportunity for the children to copy, to tell the same stories or to act out the same rhymes. They can then go on to dance and mime other stories and rhymes. For very young children, the absence of the spoken word can often be less threatening and more inviting than stories which are acted using words and voice. This can lead to the growth of language and literacy, as the children eagerly talk about what they have seen, and eventually start to read the familiar stories and to write them down.

CARER &
PASSIVE CHILD

INTRODUCTION

Most children teach themselves to roll, creep, crawl, sit, pull themselves up to standing and to walk when they are developmentally ready to do so. However, these skills can be encouraged by helping the child to become aware of her body through:

1 Touch.

2 Stimulating her to want to move.

3 'Feeding in' the physical sensation of moving in her skin and muscles, and helping her to experience the movements before she is able to execute them independently.

4 Increasing her strength.

All the activities described below can be undertaken with children of any age who are not able to move autonomously.

Carer & Passive Child
TOUCH & MASSAGE

Most mothers receive a leaflet on leaving hospital after the delivery of their baby on the benefits of touch and massage, and it is generally accepted that these are as important to a baby as food (Montagu, 1978). There are many advantages to both child and carer. Touch and massage:

1 encourage bonding and trust;

2 develop confidence in the carer of her ability to handle a small child;

3 can help to calm an anxious or nervous child, and relieve trauma;

4 can ease minor digestive upsets and aid elimination;

5 stimulate the immune system;

6 stimulate circulation;

7 stimulate the nervous system;

8 deep-cleanse the pores of the skin;

9 visibly improve the texture of the skin;

10 increase kinaesthetic awareness of the body, a prerequisite for independent movement;

11 are pleasurable for both child and carer.

Ensure that your hands are warm. Use the palm of your hand, being careful not to 'knead' or poke with your fingers or thumb. Hold the child gently, yet firmly enough to give a feeling of security. Do not inhibit movement which the child herself instigates. Be sensitive to her needs and desires. She will communicate by her movements and her facial expression whether she is enjoying an activity.

Provide a warm temperature, in a draught-free room, with no distractions such as the telephone. When room temperature allows, remove as much of the child's clothing as possible.

Repeat each movement several times while the child is enjoying it, but be ready to move on to another one as soon as she loses interest or is not comfortable. Some movements are best undertaken sitting on a chair, others sitting or lying next to the child on a bed, or on a soft mat or towel on the floor. Maintain eye contact throughout, unless the child is visibly uncomfortable with this. Talk to her gently throughout.

Ensure that both sides of the body are massaged or moved equally. Some practitioners recommend the use of massage oils. These are not essential, and can complicate and lengthen the process for a busy carer. Activities involving touch are of special benefit to children born through Caesarean section, as many of these will not have experienced the massage induced by contractions and the birth process.

Do not insist on touch and massage activities if the child resists. If the child is ill, she may not want to be massaged, although being held will be comforting for her. When holding the child, do so on your left side, as the sound of your heartbeat is reassuring and calming.

AIMS

To increase awareness of the skin and body and, through them, of self. To stimulate development in general.

Movements

1 ***Neck & Shoulders***
Lay the child on a bed. Sit behind her head, and gently rub the neck downwards from ears to shoulders, then downwards from chin to chest.

2 ***Head***
Using a circular movement, gently massage
(a) the crown of the head,
(b) down the sides of the face,
(c) the forehead, outwards from the centre to either side,
(d) the cheeks and ears, stroking lightly.

3 ***Back***
Sit or lie next to the child. Lay her on her side and, using a circular motion, stroke her upper back. Make the same circular movement to massage her lower back and the base of her spine. Lay her on her other side and repeat both activities.

4 ***Arms***
Gently stroke down the arm from the shoulder to the fingertips. Repeat with the other arm.

Development
Using fingers above the arm, and thumb below, gently squeeze all along the arm, from shoulder to fingertips. Be careful to squeeze the whole arm rather than a small amount of flesh to avoid pinching, and do not press hard.

5 ***Chest & Abdomen***
Gently stroke the chest, working down the ribs. Then stroke the abdomen, executing small circles, gradually increasing their size as you work outwards.

6 ***Feet & Toes***
Gently rub the feet, starting at the heel and working towards the toes. Massage each toe individually.

P

7 Legs

Stroke down the leg, starting at the top, from thigh to knee, and then down the shins, then round to the calves and the ankles. Repeat on the other leg.

Development

Using fingers and thumb, gently squeeze all along the leg from the top downwards. Repeat on the other leg.

8 Back

Lie on your back, with the child lying on you face down, and massage her back with alternate hands, stroking down her body.

More energetic activities involving touch include the following:

1 Massage each toe individually and firmly. Sing an appropriate song such as 'This Little Piggy'.

2 Blow raspberries on the child's feet. Then, with your lips, nibble her toes.

3 Gently but firmly massage each finger and stroke the palm of the hand. Sing an appropriate song such as 'Round and Round the Garden'.

4 Blow raspberries on her tummy. With your lips, pretend to 'eat' her tummy, chest, arms, legs, feet and neck.

Carer & Passive Child
ROCKING

At an early stage of development rocking is an activity which children particularly enjoy. It:

◆ gives a feeling of security;

◆ can calm them down if they are upset or excited;

◆ helps the child to keep her head stable;

◆ develops a feeling of trust which leads to self-confidence;

◆ allows the child to move the whole body as a unit, thus stimulating the awareness of self and of being.

AIM

To give the child the experience of moving in a rhythmic way.

Movements

1 Hold the child horizontally and securely in your arms. Sway from side to side, rocking her rhythmically towards her feet and up again. Keep eye contact throughout.

2 Stand, holding the child vertically, and gently bend your knees and straighten them rhythmically as you sing.

Development

(a) As the child grows, increase the extent of the rocking.

(b) Sit on a chair, with the child sitting facing you on your lap. Hold your arms firmly behind her back and head. Rock gently forwards and backwards, singing 'Seesaw'. Keep eye contact.

(c) Sit on the edge of a bed, holding the child firmly behind her back and head. Rock until she is upside down as you lean forward, and then lying on top of you as you rock back onto your back. Sing 'Seesaw'.

Some children avert their eyes to avoid looking at you. If this happens, encourage eye contact by looking at her fleetingly and then looking away. Repeat this, gradually extending the length of time you look at her. Be sensitive to her needs and do not distress her by insisting on eye contact before she is ready for it.

(d) Sit on the floor with legs outstretched, with the child sitting on your thighs. Holding behind her head and back, gently and rhythmically rock backwards and forwards until she is lying back on your lower legs.

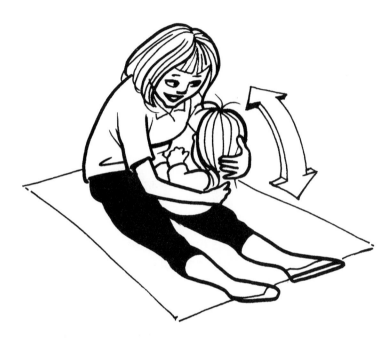

(e) In this lying position, allow the child to hold your fingers tightly to help her as she sits up.

Additional benefits

Increased awareness and strength of the stomach.
For further expansion, see Sections 4 and 7.

AIMS

1 To help the child feel her whole body moving as a unit.

2 To strengthen the muscles of stomach and arms.

3 To increase the child's ability to move rhythmically with you.

4 To encourage the child to relate to you.

Movements

1 Sit on the floor with legs outstretched, with the child sitting astride your legs. Hold hands, and rock backwards and forwards, gradually increasing the extent of the rocking.

2 Sit on the floor with the child on your lap, with her back to you. Rock backwards and forwards, singing 'Row the Boat'. On the last line, lie down, with the child lying on top of you. Later she will enjoy doing this on her own.

Additional benefits

The child's growing awareness of her back as she feels its contact with you, and later with the floor.

Carer & Passive Child
ROCKING FROM SIDE TO SIDE

AIM

To help the child experience moving from side to side.

Movement

Sit on a chair or on the floor, holding the child with her back to you, with arms around her stomach. Gently sway from side to side, singing 'Row the Boat'.

Development

Sit on floor, with the child between your legs. Sway in a more extreme manner, falling gently to one side and then the other, rhythmically, saying, "Rock, rock, rock, fall". Alternatively, sing 'Row the Boat', falling to the side on the last line, as above.

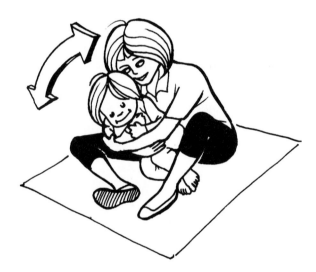

Additional benefits

(a) Rhythmic movement is calming, and helpful for those who have excess energy, or who are over-anxious.

(b) The falls to the side, which end with contact with the floor, develop awareness of the hips and sides. This is a difficult part of the body to become aware of.

Carer & Passive Child
BOUNCING

AIMS

As children develop, they increasingly enjoy the activity and rhythm of bouncing, the aims of which are:

1 to help them develop a sense of weight;

2 to further enhance the feeling of moving as a unit;

3 to increase the awareness of who they are.

The following activities give the experience of bouncing up and down. Gradually a child will begin to bounce by herself, without the carer's help (see Section 2). Bouncing also strengthens the muscles of the legs and feet, and uses the knees, thus increasing awareness of them.

Preparatory Activity

With the child lying on her back, press your hands gently against her feet, encouraging her to press back against your hands.

Movements

1 Sit on a chair with the child sitting facing you and hold her securely round the waist. Bounce your thighs up and down gently. There are a number of traditional songs to sing, such as 'Ride a Cock Horse'.

Development

Increase the extent of the bounces, to the song 'A lady goes a trot, a trot'. This traditional song can be altered in any way you choose. For example, use the child's name throughout. See Appendix I.

2 Sit, holding the child round the waist facing you, as if she is standing on your thighs. Bounce her up and down, making sure that she does not put too much weight on her legs.

Developments

(a)   As above, but let her bounce.
(b)   As above, but allow her to grasp your hands.

3 Sit with one thigh crossed over the other. The child sits on the ankle of your raised foot. Hold her hands firmly and bounce your raised foot up and down. Sing 'Ride a Cock Horse', or a similar song.

Additional benefits

Bounces will lead to jumps, which are a developmental milestone. If you have access to a trampoline, let the child sit on it, and help her to bounce. She will eventually stand on it. Help her again. Bouncing on this can help the child acquire the feeling, and eventually the skill, of jumping. (See Section 3 for jumps.)

Carer & Passive Child
ROLLING

AIMS

1 To increase awareness of the body through the contact of each body part with the surface on which she is lying.

2 To encourage the child to move independently.

3 To help the child to become aware of turning.

Movement

Lie the child on her back on a firm surface, for example on a mat on the floor. Sitting a little distance away on the floor, make a noise to one side of her head, and then the other, to encourage her to move her head to see what is making the noise.

Development

(a) Place toys just out of reach on one side of the child and then the other, to encourage her to reach to the side, and eventually to roll over in order to reach them.

(b) Lay the child on the floor and, with your hands on her left hip and shoulder, gently tilt her to the left. Repeat to the right side.

(c) Increase the tilt, rolling the child until she is on her side. Repeat to other side.

(d) Repeat the above activity, rolling until the child is on her stomach, and then on her back again. Repeat to the other side.

(e) Sit on the floor with legs outstretched, with the child lying across your legs. Gently roll her continuously down your legs to your feet and then back up again towards you, by pushing on her hips and shoulders.

(f) Lie on your back on the floor, with the child lying on top of you, face to face, and hold her across her back and hips. Gently rock from side to side, gradually rocking further and further to the sides as the child becomes more confident.

(g) Lay the child on the floor and crouch down next to her. Making sure her arms are up above her head, so as not to get squashed, gently roll her along the floor.

For further expansions see Section 4.

AIM

Development of the awareness of moving the arms.

Movements

1 Lay the child on her back, with her hands grasping your thumbs. Stretch her arms above her head, and then down again.

Development

Stretch one of the child's arms above her head, then the other as the first arm is brought down. Some development is needed before a child can move each arm separately and independently. Help her to experience this, but do not insist or even ask for it in the early stages.

2 Hold the child sitting or standing with her back to you, stretch her arms out to the sides, and then across her chest. Repeat.

Considerable maturity is needed before a child can cross her arms across the centre line of her body by herself. This activity will help develop this skill.

For further expansion of arm movements see Sections 2 and 3.

Carer & Passive Child
BIRDS & AEROPLANES

AIMS

1 To encourage the child to raise her head.

2 To strengthen her back.

3 To enhance eye contact.

Movement

Lie on the floor with your knees up by your chest. Lay the child on your shins. Gently move your legs forward and back. Stretch her arms out to her sides 'like an aeroplane', then bring them in again. Repeat.

Additional benefit

This activity allows the child to see you from an unusual angle: she is looking down on you. This strengthens her awareness of different levels.

P

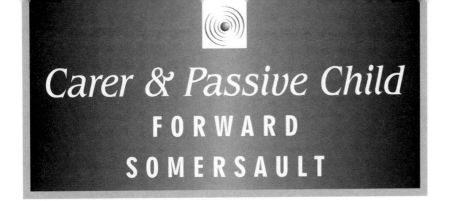

Carer & Passive Child
FORWARD
SOMERSAULT

AIM

To increase the child's awareness of her centre as it turns upside down.

Movement

Sit on the floor with the child standing behind you. Help her to lean over you, putting her tummy on your shoulder and tucking her head in, making her body curved. Hold one hand behind her head, the other on the small of her back, and gently help her to do a forward somersault over your shoulder, finishing sitting in front of you. Ensure that her body is curved, and that she is fully supported throughout.

17

Carer & Passive Child
CATERPILLARS

AIM

Increased awareness of the stomach and knees.

Movement

Gently place the child on her stomach on the floor, with her hands near her shoulders. Help her to lift her stomach as you bring her knees under it. Walk her hands forward. Repeat the activity, encouraging her vocally throughout. Eventually, she will be able and eager to 'be a caterpillar' by herself.

This activity requires strength and physical control and awareness. It takes a long time to master.

Carer & Passive Child
CRAWLING

AIM

The development of cross-lateral skills. Crawling is an activity which most children undertake independently when they are developmentally ready. There is no need to teach it, but helping the child to experience the movement can be helpful and enjoyable. Crawling also increases mobility of the spine.

Crawling involves cross-lateral movement (the use of the right arm with the left leg, and the left arm with the right leg). Some children miss out this stage of development entirely, with no adverse effects whatsoever.

Movement

Place the child on her hands and knees, and put a toy a little in front of her, just out of reach. Gently move her right knee forward, then her left hand, then her left knee, then her right hand. Repeat this several times on several occasions. Do not insist if she does not crawl but prefers to lie on her stomach to reach the toy.

Additional benefits

1 Increased awareness of the knees as they come in contact with the floor.

2 Increased strength of stomach muscles.

3 Increased strength in arms and shoulders.

SIMPLE MOVEMENTS WHICH THE CARER HELPS THE CHILD TO EXECUTE

INTRODUCTION

Ayoung child experiences and learns about herself and the world through her body. It is through growing self-awareness and control of the body that self-esteem will develop. Movement is therefore very helpful for the future growth of physically able children.

The following activities are developments of those described in Section 1. The intention is that those children who are physically able will begin to execute movements of their own accord, leading eventually to reduced dependency and gradually enhancing their growing sense of self.

Physically disabled children, who cannot move by themselves or who have pain doing so, will benefit from being moved by their carer. Many of the activities described in this section can be undertaken with physically handicapped children, whose strength, awareness of the body and sense of self will be gradually enhanced.

Always watch carefully, and encourage and praise the child when she improves or succeeds in a task. This will help her gain confidence. Do not criticize. Always place yourself at the same level as the child. If she is sitting on the floor, do so too. Never talk down to her.

Many local authorities in the UK, and parks and recreation districts in the USA, now provide gymnastic classes for very young children. (Contact yours for addresses.) These give access to a variety of suitable equipment for climbing on, over and through, and can be beneficial and fun, and a useful adjunct to the activities described in this book. In Germany, movement activities are part of the nursery curriculum.

In most areas, playgrounds can be found where children can climb ramps and ladders, crawl through tunnels, slide down slides, bounce, swing and seesaw. These too are fun, and are very helpful in developing a child's strength, co-ordination and confidence. Toy cars which the child can propel more by walking rather than by pedalling, and tricycles on which the pedals can be activated by pushing the child, are both useful in this respect.

However, the best climbing frame is an adult, and none of the activities described above can quite match the advantage of movements undertaken by a child together with a carer, as this also enhances trust and relationship skills.

Simple Movements
PUSHING

AIMS

1 To increase strength in, and awareness of, the legs and feet.

2 To stimulate consciousness of the connection between the legs and the body.

3 To encourage the use of the stomach, thus increasing awareness of self.

4 To help the child become aware of her back, as she feels its contact with what she is lying on.

5 To establish and increase eye contact where necessary.

Movements

1 Lay the child on a bed or mat. Sit at her feet, facing her. Establish eye contact, talking and telling her what is happening. Pick up her feet and put gentle pressure on them with your hands, encouraging her to press back. Press so that both legs bend, but gently enough for her to be able to push your hands away again as she straightens her legs. Repeat as often as she enjoys the activity.

Variations

For those children who are uncomfortable with eye contact, do not maintain this for more than a couple of seconds. If you keep looking away, the child will feel more confident about looking at you.

For those children who do not want to lie down or who continually avoid eye contact, the activity can be performed with the child sitting on your lap with her back to you.

2 Place the child's feet on your chest and exert gentle pressure by slowly moving your torso gently forward and back.

Development

(a) Lay the child on the floor without a mat. Remember to ensure that the floor is smooth, not cold, and splinter-free. Encourage her to push your hands away, but this time do not move them. The result will be that she slides backwards on her back by her own efforts, thus increasing awareness of her back. Gently pull her towards you again. Repeat.

(b) Stand up and, with the child lying down, hold her by her ankles, and gently pull her along the floor.

(c) The child will often develop this on her own initiative, and will travel around the room on her back 'like a shark'.

3 Lay the child on a mat, bed or floor. Holding her feet, help her to 'bicycle'.

Development

(a) Encourage the child to 'bicycle' alone.

(b) Sit facing the child, both with legs outstretched. Gently press against her feet with your feet, and move them from side to side, encouraging her to press back.

Additional benefit

Development of social skills as the child moves in relation to another person.

For further expansion see Section 4.

Simple Movements
BOUNCING

AIMS

To encourage independent movement, self-confidence and self-awareness.

Movement

Allow the child to bounce on a bed. Access to a trampoline (a small one, with a handrail) is useful at this stage, as the slightest movement by the child is enlarged, thus enhancing the experience of bouncing, which the child later will be able to initiate herself. Sing 'Five Little Monkeys' to accompany the movement.

Simple Movements
CATERPILLARS

(See Section 1)

AIMS

1 To stimulate independent movement.

2 To increase awareness of the torso, knees and arms.

Movement

Encourage the child to move by herself 'like a caterpillar'. Help her to lie on the floor on her stomach, then to bring her knees under it, and then to stretch out one arm and then the other, until she is lying on the floor on her stomach again. Comment on what she is doing.

P

Simple Movements
LIZARDS

© Naomi Benari, 1999

AIMS

1 Increased awareness of the stomach, as it slides on the floor.

2 Development of cross-lateral skills.

Movement

Place the child on her stomach on the floor. Show her, by gently placing her body in the relevant position, how to crawl 'like a lizard'. Stretch one arm in front of her, and bend the other knee up next to her chest. Help her to pull herself along. Now stretch out the other arm, and bend the other knee. Repeat, encouraging her vocally, until she can do it by herself.

Simple Movements
WALKING ON THE BOTTOM

AIM

To increase awareness of the bottom. Most children crawl as their first method of locomotion. However, some very young children teach themselves to bounce along on their bottom instead. This gives them the advantage of seeing clearly where they are going, as well as increasing awareness of that part of the body.

Movements

1 Encourage the child to rotate on her bottom.

2 Sit on the floor with the child between your legs and with her back to you. Walk forward, then backwards, on your bottom, using your legs and feet to propel yourself, encouraging her to do the same.

3 Encourage the child to undertake this by herself.

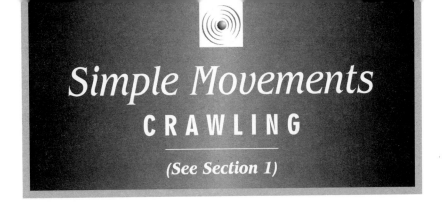

Simple Movements
CRAWLING

(See Section 1)

Children start to crawl because of their desire to get around and to become independent. Crawling is very empowering and gives great joy.

AIMS

1 To increase independent activity.

2 To develop cross-lateral movement.

3 To increase awareness of the knees and arms.

Movement

Place the child on her hands and knees, and put a toy a little in front of her, just out of reach. Do not insist if she cannot crawl or reach the toy. Give it to her.

Development

(a) Encourage the child to crawl 'like a dog' or 'like a cat'. Comment on the movement qualities required. For example, the cat moves with smooth, gliding movements.

Additional benefit

Increased awareness of the knees.

(b) Ask the child to stretch 'like a cat', arching her back until it is hollow, and then rising on her toes and hands, and arching her back the other way.

Additional benefit

This will increase mobility and awareness of the back and stomach.

Simple Movements
WHOLE BODY AWARENESS

You will need:

Several hoops
A bean bag

AIM

To increase awareness of the whole body.

Movements

1 Hold as many hoops as you can vertically on the floor, and ask the child to crawl through them.

2 Put the hoops down on the floor, spaced out. Ask the child:

(a) to pick one up and to slide it down her body;

(b) to stand in one hoop and to raise it until it is over her head.

(For expansion of this activity in groups see Section 4.)

3 Ask the child to sit and:

(a) to put a bean bag on her head;

(b) to hold it

under her chin without dropping it,

under one arm,

between her knees,

between her feet.

Development

(a) Ask the child to walk with the bean bag:

under her chin,

under one arm.

(b) Ask her to jump with it between her knees. (This is easier than walking.)

Simple Movements
SITTING, STANDING & WALKING

Most children find their own way of rolling onto their stomachs, and sitting. They then begin to pull themselves up on nearby furniture or adults. Supervise this, giving them access to safe objects such as coffee tables or sofas.

NB Make sure that the surface on which they stand is not slippery or that, if it is, they wear shoes, just in case they lose their balance and hit their chin or mouth on the table top.

The child then begins to walk along, holding on as she goes. You can help by offering the child your hands, and supporting her firmly, walking along behind her. The final exciting stage is when you can kneel down a few feet away and invite her to cover the space between you by herself. Gradually increase the space. Provide pull-along toys to encourage independent walking.

Simple Movements
ROLE REVERSAL ACTIVITIES

In any of the games outlined below the roles can be reversed, with the child encouraged to manipulate or move the carer.

AIMS

1 To increase the child's self-confidence.

2 To enhance awareness of herself and of her own strength.

3 To allow her to look after someone else.

Movements

Game 1

Encourage the child to sit with knees very bent, holding her arms around her calves. Gently try to 'unfold' the 'parcel', as she tries to maintain her position.

Game 2

Sit on the floor with the child sitting in front of you, with her back to you and her knees up under her chin and her arms around her legs. Put your arms around her and encourage her to 'escape' from the 'house'. Talk and joke about what you are doing to ensure that she understands that this is a game, and that she does not become alarmed.

Benefits

The strength needed to remain curled up as you try to uncurl her, and that needed to try to 'escape', as well as the physical contact with you, will strengthen the child's muscles and increase her awareness of her body, particularly her tummy and chest.

As she develops, she could play these games, supervised, with a peer.

Simple Movements
AWARENESS OF THE FACE

AIM

To increase awareness of the face and its expressive possibilities.

Movements

1 Touch the different parts of the face.

2 Smile, then pout. Repeat.

3 Frown ('pretend to be angry'), then raise the eyebrows ('pretend to be surprised').

4 Screw eyes tight shut, then open them wide.

5 (Try to) open one eye at a time.

6 Wrinkle the nose and relax it.

Simple Movements
AWARENESS OF THE HANDS

Control of the hands is essential for work and play.

AIMS

1 Awareness of hands and fingers.

2 Development of fine motor control.

Many soft toys are designed to increase the sensitivity to different textures. If these are not available, use household objects of varying textures.

Give the child the opportunity to squeeze a sponge or rubber ball.

Hand painting and working with modelling clay or *Plasticine* also increase awareness of the hands.

Threading objects onto a string increases fine motor control. (Be careful that the objects are not small enough for a small child to swallow.) **Only attempt this activity when the child has reached the age when she no longer puts things into her mouth.**

Movements

1 Open the fingers wide, stretching the hands and making then stiff. Close them again making tight fists.

Development

Hold the fists in front of the body. Open each finger in turn starting with the thumb. Then close them again, one by one.

2 Make the hands floppy and shake them in front of the body, at the side, high above the head, low near the ground.

3 Rub the hands (then the arms, legs, tummies). Sing 'Here we go round the Mulberry Bush', holding hands and walking round each other on the chorus, and 'washing' on the verses.

Additional benefit

Increased awareness of direction and space.

4 Wiggle the fingers, as if playing the piano.

5 Sing action songs which require the movement of the hands and of the fingers in varying ways: for example, 'Two Little Dicky Birds', 'Twinkle, Twinkle, Little Star', 'One Finger, One Thumb'.

Variations

Play, and then pretend to play, different musical instruments: for example, the triangle, drum, flute, guitar.
Sing, with actions, 'We are the Music Men'.

Additional benefits

(a) By learning to use her fingers to illustrate a song, a child is gaining co-ordination and control.

(b) Use of words to music, with rhythmic movement, utilizes both hemispheres of the brain simultaneously, leading to integration.

CLAPPING

At first a small child will not unfold the fingers enough to be able to clap. Compare her hand size with yours, and massage, rub and play with her hands (see Section 1), to help her become aware of them.

Give her toys which can be taken apart and put together, also those which can be sorted according to size and shape (see Appendix I for suppliers).

Movement

Hold the child's wrists, as you clap her hands, singing suitable songs, such as 'Clap hands, Daddy come home'.

Development

(a) Encourage the child to clap her own hands in time with the song.

(b) Encourage the child to clap on your hands.

(c) Invent games where you and the child clap your hands and those of each other.

Additional benefit

Clapping while singing or listening to songs helps to develop a sense of rhythm.

Simple Movements
AWARENESS
OF THE ARMS

Arms are necessary for reaching, hugging, pushing and pulling.

AIM

To develop awareness of the arms. Provide toys which necessitate pushing, pulling and lifting.

Movements

1 Encourage the child to rub one arm with the fingers of the other hand, gently, from the fingertips to the shoulder and down again. Rotate the arm, so that the other side of the arm is uppermost, and repeat. Change arms, and repeat with the other hand.

2 Encourage the child to press the fingers of one hand gently on the other hand, working gradually up the arm to the shoulder and down again. Rotate the arm, and repeat with the underarm uppermost. Change arms and repeat with the other hand.

3 Slowly raise both arms in front of the body until they are above the head, then slowly lower them again. Repeat this, raising the arms sideways from the body.

Variation

Raise both arms fast in front of the body until they are above the head, then lower them fast. Repeat sideways from the body.

Development

Raise one arm high to the side as the other is brought down next to the body. Reverse, raising the other arm. Allow the body to tilt in sympathy with the movement.

The ability to move one arm at a time is a question of development. Do not be discouraged if a child cannot yet execute this movement on her own. Hold her hands and help her to experience moving in this way.

See Section 3 for further developments.

Simple Movements
AWARENESS OF THE FEET

We take feet for granted, but they are essential for locomotion.

AIM

Development of awareness of the feet, and of what they are able to do.

Movements

1 Ask the child to sit and to gently rub her feet all over, top and bottom, including each toe individually: first one foot, then the other.

2 Stretch out the legs in front of the body. Turn the feet up towards the ceiling and down towards the floor. Repeat.

3 With the child's legs stretched out in front of her body, turn the feet from side to side, outwards and then inwards, several times.

Development

(a) Rotate the feet in parallel, both to one side and then to the other, like windscreen wipers.

(b) Encourage the child to do this on her own.

(c) Ask the child to lie down. Lift her legs at right angles to her body. Take them from side to side, like giant windscreen wipers.

(d) Encourage the child to do this on her own.

(e) Ask the child to stand on her toes, stretching up high, then to stand on her heels.

(f) Ask her to stamp her feet alternately.

Development

4 Ask the child to travel across the room

   (a) walking on her toes, stretching up high;

   (b) walking on her heels only;

   (c) sliding her feet 'as if you are skating, or skiing, or walking on ice';

   (d) lifting her feet delicately, 'creeping quietly, like a mouse'.

Additional benefit

This increases control and confirms to you that mastery of the feet has been achieved.

5 Provide materials of varying textures on which to walk.

Simple Movements
TURNING AND TWISTING

Most children love to turn, and will do so as soon as they feel confident enough. It gives them a changing view of the world and helps them to feel in control of it. It is exciting. Sometimes they will turn without realizing the consequences. Be ready to catch and stop them before they become so dizzy that they fall over. (See Section 3 for variations on this theme.)

AIM

To increase awareness of the centre of the body.

Movement

Stand the child with feet apart, and gently twist her shoulders to one side, swinging the arms in the same direction. Repeat to the other side.

Additional benefit

Self-awareness and confidence will be enhanced as mobility of the centre of the body increases.

Simple Movements
BODY AWARENESS: SIZE & SHAPE

AIM

To develop awareness of body, size and shape.

With the use of simple props, it is possible to help the child become aware of her whole body and the shapes it can make. For example:

draw round her as she lies on a piece of paper;
ask her to lie inside a hoop;
place a ribbon or rope on the floor in a curve, and ask her to lie on it.

Movement

Encourage the child to curl up in a tiny ball on the floor. Ask her to slowly, gradually, 'grow big and tall' until she is standing on the balls of her feet, arms stretched up. Ask her to slowly curl down again.

Development

(a) Ask your child to grow into a particular shape:

a tall thin shape, 'like a pencil or a pin';

a wide shape, 'like a gate';

a round shape 'like a ball'.

(b) Musical statues: the child dances and when the music or drumming stops, she has to freeze in a designated shape:
tall and thin, fat/wide, round, spiky, funny.

(c) Ask the child to walk using large steps, then tiny ones.

(d) Ask her to dance using large arm movements.

Additional benefits

(a) Increased awareness and control of the body.

(b) Development of body image.

Simple Movements
SPEED

AIM

To develop awareness of tempo.

Movements

1 Ask the child to walk round the room to the beating of a drum. Gradually speed up the drumming, saying "Faster, faster." Then gradually slow it down, saying, "Slower, slower."

Variations

As above, but (a) crawling; (b) jumping; (c) stretching up to the ceiling, down to the floor, slowly, then quickly.

Development

Ask the child to walk or crawl quickly then slowly, without the help of the drum beat.

2 Pond Game

The child sits on the floor with knees pulled up near the chest, opposite the carer, 'next to a pond in which there lives a fish who wants to bite people's toes'. Slowly both walk their feet into the pond, feeling for the fish. When the legs are straight, the carer shouts 'Fish!' and both quickly withdraw their feet very fast. This game can be played in a group, with the children taking it in turns to do the shouting.

Additional benefit

Control.

MORE DEMANDING MOVEMENTS FOR THE CHILD TO EXECUTE INDEPENDENTLY

INTRODUCTION

Children enjoy play, and will usually respond well if, from the very earliest age, every task is presented as a game. As they grow, they will bring their imagination into the project, and will make up their own games. Piaget talked about three periods of child development: sensorimotor, concrete and formal (Witkin, 1974). Children will enjoy 'being' rabbits or cats, and later they will want to move 'like' a horse or a tree in the wind. (Older children will enjoy moving in the same way that an animal moves.)

For young children, movements which are motivated by an image will be richer and more varied than those which occur simply because of an instruction to, for example, 'move fast'. There are several benefits:

1 This can develop the imagination.

2 It can evoke a range of feelings.

3 It can give an opportunity to use and enhance the emotions: the excitement of moving fast like a horse, the drama of a chase, fear (a tiny amount) as a small animal escapes; and so on.

However, it is advisable to ensure that a child is also told or reminded about the movement quality (sharp, smooth, strong, weak), speed (fast, slow), direction (forward, back, round) and level (high, low) of the animal or person she is portraying. There are several reasons for this. First, it ensures a more precise portrayal. Also very often children will copy correctly the shape of an animal or person they are 'being' or imitating, because they have seen a picture of it, but they will not move like the animal if they have never seen it move. It can be useful to show videos of animals moving, or to take children to the zoo.

Second, it has the important advantage of increasing the child's awareness of her own body, and enhancing her self-esteem as she realizes with pride that she can control it, and make it move in any way she wants.

Finally, it encourages creativity and imagery, as the child endeavours to move like known phenomena.

The activities and movements outlined below are designed to help develop body awareness. They can be undertaken on a one-to-one basis with a carer, or can be done in a group with several children. As a child's body awareness grows, so her confidence will increase. This will lead to her taking the initiative and moving in her own way rather than acting only on your suggestions.

As suggested earlier, children who cannot initiate movements by themselves can participate in all these activities, either by being held as the carer moves, or by being pushed in their buggies. In this way they will experience the sensation of moving in different directions and in different ways.

Visually impaired children can also take part. At first they can be led and guided: stand behind the child, with your right hand on her shoulder and your left holding her left hand; gradually let go of her shoulder and, standing in front of her, hold both hands; then hold only one hand. Eventually, she will feel confident enough to dance, for example, without help.

Children learn first through body experience, and cognitive development also starts from this (Leventhal, 1974). This section starts with activities which help the child to achieve self-awareness and control, and ends with descriptions of activities which stimulate cognitive development.

More Demanding Movements
CONTROL

AIM

To develop control of the body and emotions.

Movement

This can be undertaken with a child on her own and, later, in a small group. Ask the child or children to walk across or around the room, and to stop when you bang a drum or clap, or make some other sudden noise.

Variation

Repeat as above, but ask the child to run or dance, rather than to walk.

Development

Repeat the above activity, but asking the child to stop when you say, 'Stop'. When working with a group, let the children take turns in saying, 'Stop'.

Additional benefits

(a)   This activity increases listening skills.

(b)   It may encourage reluctant talkers to join in and say 'Stop'.

(c)   It helps to increase feelings of self-esteem as the child 'controls' not only herself but others.

Variations

Ask the children to sit down when the music stops.

Use a drum or play music, asking the children to dance to it, and to stop (freeze) in whatever position they are in when the music stops, and to hold that position.

As above, but ask them to adopt a specific shape when the music stops: for example, wide, round, thin, funny (see 'Shape', p60).

As above, but ask them to stand on one leg when the music stops.

Additional benefit

This will indicate to you how much control and balance the child has acquired.

Ask the child to stand with legs slightly apart. Encourage her:

◆ to nod her head up and down, looking at the ceiling and then the floor

◆ turn it from side to side

◆ to wobble it, so that the top of the head goes from side to side.

(Do not encourage circling the head, as this can lead to dizziness.)

More Demanding Movements
HIPS & TUMMIES

(Children usually respond better to 'tummy' than to 'hips'.)
Ask the child to stand with her hands on her waist, legs apart. Encourage her to move her hips and tummy several times in each direction:

1 side to side;

2 forward and back;

3 in a circle;

4 in a circle the other way.

More Demanding Movements
K N E E S

AIM

To increase awareness and mobility of the knees. This will eventually facilitate jumping.

Movements

1 Ask the child to sit with legs stretched out in front of her. Ask her to:

1) pat the knees, tickle them, rub them, scratch them.

2) bends them until the knees are tight against the chest. Slowly stretch them out again until the knees 'disappear'. Repeat.

2 Encourage the child to crawl 'like a cat'. If asked, provide her with 'pretend' milk and food. Stroke her as she crawls to you.

3 Encourage the child to walk on her knees, 'like a tiny person'. **Note:** while this activity is painful for adults, most children enjoy it very much. However, if the child does not want to do it, do not force or even encourage her to do so.

4 Encourage the child to walk with knees totally bent, so that her knees are almost touching her chest, 'like a duck'.

Development

Sing 'Five little ducks went swimming', pointing out the contrast between the tiny legs and those used when 'flying' or 'swimming'.

5 Walk with wobbly knees 'like a scarecrow', then with stiff knees 'like a robot'.

Development

Make a dance about scarecrows and robots, asking the children to move appropriately, as you make appropriate sounds: for example, three beats of scarecrow wobbles, pause, four beats of robot walks.

Additional benefit

Increases listening skills, as the children respond to the sounds or music.

6 Ask the child to find different ways to use her knees as she walks. For example:

(a) knees stuck together,

(b) knees far away from each other,

(c) knees bent,

(d) lifting knees towards the chest, marching.

More Demanding Movements
A R M S

AIM

Increase awareness and strength of the arms.

Movements

1 Ask the child to lean on a wall with the arms outstretched while you count up to three. Gradually increase this, counting up to four, five or six;

2 Ask her to walk around the room on hands and feet.

3 Put the child's hands in the loops at either end of the elastic. Help her to pull her hands away from each other, and then allow them to be pulled close again. Repeat several times.

Variation

Start with one hand a few inches above the other. Encourage her to raise the top hand, thus lifting the other one. Repeat with the other hand uppermost.

See Section 4 on children working in pairs in similar activities.

4 Ask the child to stand with her arms at her sides. Ask her to raise her arms sideways, leading first with the elbows, then the wrists and finally unfolding the fingers. Lower the arms in the same way, leading first with the elbows, then the wrists and finally lowering the fingers.

Variation

Ask the child to cross her arms in front of the body. Ask her to slowly unfold them, extending them to the sides, then to slowly fold them up again across the body. Encourage her to allow the body to open out and curl up with the arm movement.

Development

Repeat all the activities, first with one arm then the other. The ability to do this will depend on the degree of maturity of each child, and will increase with repetition. However, do not insist on repetition if a child really cannot do it, as this will decrease her self-esteem.

You will need:

some lengths of elastic about 2 cm wide and 45 cm long, with loops at either end, wide enough for a child to insert her hand and curl her fingers around it

More Demanding Movements
SWINGS

This can be a difficult activity, as it requires tension to raise the arms, and relaxation as they drop. The feeling of the weight of the body and the flow of movement is very enjoyable.

AIMS

To encourage risk-taking and an ability to let go.
To increase awareness of the arms.

Movements

1 Ask the child to swing the arms up and down, with a strong impetus to start.

Development

(a) Encourage her to repeat as above, but bending the knees as the arms reach her sides again, then to swing the arms up strongly, so that the heels leave the ground, and the body is suspended for a second on the toes.

(b) Ask her to repeat as above, pushing the floor away with the feet as the arms start their upward swing, and allowing the swing to lift the body into the air in a jump.

Variation

Repeat as above, asking the child to jump in different ways. For example: feet together, apart, scissor jumps (see 'Jumps', below).

2 Ask the child to swing the arms from side to side horizontally, with a strong impetus to start.

Development

Ask her to swing the arms side to side, bending the knees at the end of each swing. Encourage her to make the third swing strong, so that it turns the body, which executes a complete turn on one foot.

3 Ask the child to start with the arms down in front of the body, and then to swing them up to one side and then the other, bending the knees as the arms are lowered in front of the body as they swing in a 'u' shape.

Development

As above, making the third swing strong, this time allowing it to move the body to the side, either in a lean, or onto one leg, or in a jump. Encourage the children to 'see what happens'.

4 Ask the child to stand with the arms at the sides of the body. Ask her to swing the arms forwards to horizontal and back behind the body, bending the knees as the arms pass the body. On the third swing (the second swing forward), encourage her to allow the body to be moved forward in a jump. Let her repeat the action, starting the first swing backwards, and jumping backwards.

Additional Benefits

(a) Increasing the strength of the third swing results in a rhythmic sequence of movements, thus enhancing the child's awareness of rhythm, and giving a feeling of security.

(b) The strong movements which result from the third swing will make the child aware of her own strength and power, thus strengthening her self-esteem.

5 Ask the child to move her arms in as many different ways as she can find.

More Demanding Movements
JUMPS

Jumping is an activity which depends on the development of the child. It cannot be taught if the child is not ready, but acquisition of the skill can be helped. See Sections 1 and 2 for bounces with a carer, on a bed and on a trampoline. It involves risk and courage, as the jumper loses contact with the floor.

AIM

To increase the ability to jump by finding different ways of doing so.

Once a child is able to jump, most greatly enjoy the activity. It is then possible to discuss different ways of jumping. Start by making suggestions yourself, gradually drawing ideas from the child. The following examples are graded in order of development needed for their execution.

Movements

Ask the child to:

1 Jump on the spot from both feet to both feet (two to two).

2 Jump the feet apart, and then together again.

3 Open the legs sideways in the air, and land with them together.

4 Jump with one leg forward and the other back, landing with them together ('scissor jump').

5 Jump in as many ways as she can think of: for example, with legs tucked under the bottom.

6 Hop on one foot, landing on the same foot, on the spot, forwards, backwards, sideways, round and round.

7 From one foot to both feet: for example, 'over a puddle'. Stand on both feet, stretch one leg over the puddle and jump 'over the puddle', landing on both feet.

8 From two feet to one. Help her to stand on both feet, then jump, landing on one foot.

9 Include different qualities. For example,

   a) a jump with a sudden explosive beginning, as when a tiger pounces on its prey.

   b) a delicate jump, carefully, 'like a bird'.

10 Jump high.

11 Travel, forwards, backwards, sideways, round.

12 Forward 'like a kangaroo'.

13 Forward, extending the arms forward, and the legs backwards during the jump 'like a frog'.

14 With knees fully bent, crouching, 'like a duck'.

More Demanding Movements
GALLOPS & SKIPS

Galloping and skipping are movements which often happen unconsciously. However, conscious execution depends on the development of the child, who will not attempt these movements until she is ready to do so.

AIM

Increase the child's physical coordination in general.

Movements

1 Galloping

Stand facing the child, holding both hands. Step to the side with your right foot (her left), and close your left foot to it (her right). Repeat this slowly, travelling up the room, exerting a slight pull on her left arm as you step to the right. Gradually this movement can be speeded up, until you find yourselves galloping. Repeat to the other side.

2 Skipping

(a) Stand with legs apart, facing the child and holding both her hands. Slowly sway from side to side.

(b) Execute a little hop as you reach the end of each sway, encouraging her to do so by very slightly lifting her hands as you hop.

(c) Gradually increase the speed of this movement.

(d) Travel across the room moving backwards, so that the child travels forwards.

(e) Gradually reduce the space between your legs, and the size of the sways, so that eventually you are stepping backwards, and she is stepping and skipping forwards.

AIM

1 To further increase control.

2 To help develop awareness of shape.

3 To nurture the consciousness of the body in space.

Movements

1 Ask the child to sit or lie, and to make herself into a stone or rock, in any shape she chooses: long, round or spiky.

2 Ask the child to make herself into a shape which is:

(a) tall and thin, 'like a stick';

(b) wide and fat, 'like a fat man, or a gate';

(c) round, 'like a ball';

(d) spiky;

(e) funny.

Development

(a) Ask the child to repeat the shapes, to ensure that she has remembered and can duplicate them;

(b) Ask her to move across the room in these shapes.

(For expansion of this activity in groups, see Section 4.)

More Demanding Movements
S P A C E

AIM

Awareness of shape in space.

Movements

Ask the child to draw with an imaginary pencil in the air:

1 a straight line up and down, stretching up on the toes, and then touching the floor;

2 a big circle, round and round, reaching up on the toes, far to the sides, and down to the floor;

3 a line from side to side, reaching and leaning to alternate sides;

4 a wiggly line from side to side;

5 a wiggly line from above the head, standing on the toes, right down to the floor;

6 different shapes, such as triangles, squares, letters and numbers.

Development

Ask the children to make each shape using their whole body, encouraging them to stretch, bend and twist as much as possible. Awareness of the body grows through extreme, full movements rather than small gestures.

(For further developments, with props, see 'Movement in Space', in Section 4.)

AIM

To increase spatial awareness, particularly of different levels.

Movements

Encourage the child to explore the level where she is standing.

1 sweeping the arms around:
  (a) in front of her body,
  (b) at the sides of her body,
  (c) behind her.

2 moving around the room at the low level:
  (a) on bent legs,
  (b) crawling,
  (c) sliding on the tummy or back (low level),
  (d) rolling.

3 exploring the high level:
  (a) up on tip toe,
  (b) waving the arms around above the head,
  (c) jumping.

© *Naomi Benari, 1999*
You may photocopy this page for administrative use only

More Demanding Movements
TRAVELLING IN SPACE

AIM

To increase the child's awareness of space and her ability to move in it.

Movements

1 Ask the child to walk or march:

- in a straight line, up and down the room;
- in a large circle round the room;
- in a small circle, round herself;
- diagonally;
- in a wiggly line, or zigzag;
- in a square;
- in a triangle.

Physically impaired children can take part in the above activity by being carried or pushed in their buggies in different directions. (For more ideas, see Section 4.)

2 As children develop, they will become aware of the many ways of travelling from one place to another. They can be asked to suggest different methods. For example:

- crawl, slide, roll;
- walk, run, skip, gallop, jump, hop;
- walk forwards, backwards, sideways, turning;
- with large steps, tiny steps;
- with raised knees, wobbly knees, stiff knees;
- on the toes, stretched up;
- with bent knees, bent over.

3 Once children have discovered the pleasure of turning, they can be encouraged to think of different ways of doing so. For example:

- taking small steps, turning a few degrees at a time, on flat feet, or on the balls of the feet;

- standing on one foot, lifting the other, putting it down across the supporting foot, and swivelling round, fast or slow;

- jumping round;

- hopping round on one foot;

- spiralling. Children start with bent knees and lowered arms. They turn several revolutions, gradually straightening the knees and rising onto the balls of the feet, while gradually raising the arms to a point above their heads. In simpler terms, they 'start low and go higher and higher';

- the reverse of the above, starting high and going lower and lower;

- with a partner, spinning round, holding hands (see Section 4);

- in a circle with a group, walking, running, galloping or skipping round;

- on different body parts, such as the bottom, tummy, back, hands and knees, hands and feet.

4 Encourage the child to move around in a haphazard, indefinite floor pattern combining straight lines in all directions, curves and circles.

More Demanding Movements
QUALITY

Movements can be gentle, strong, direct, indirect.

AIM

To enhance awareness of different ways of moving and different qualities of movement. These movements can be executed in silence, with only the tone of the carer's voice to encourage the required quality. Alternatively, a drum or other percussive instrument can be used in some cases, or recorded music can be played.

1 Free, Gentle Movements

Speaking slowly and quietly, perhaps with slow music, ask the child to move her arms slowly and freely, folding and unfolding them, gently, without any impetus or strength 'like seaweed floating in the sea'.

Variations

Ask the child to:

Sit and do the same with the legs.
Sit and do the same with torso.
Stand, using the whole body.
Use the whole body, travelling around the room. Encourage her to use different levels: sitting, rolling on the floor, reaching up high.

Additional benefits

(a) For those who are reluctant to move, this activity is not too demanding.

(b) For those with surplus energy, it can have a calming effect.

(c) For those with low muscle tone, it can increase self-confidence, as it requires no more strength than they have, and they can execute the task with ease.

(d) It induces a feeling of gentleness and caring.

2 Strong Movements

Ask the child, either on your command or to a drumbeat:

(a) to stamp her feet;

(b) to push a wall or an object strongly with her arms;

(c) punch one fist strongly into the air above the head, then the other, then to punch forward, then to the side.

Developments

(a) Let the child choose the direction in which she directs her punches.

(b) Let her do the same with the feet, either standing or sitting, kicking them in different directions.

(c) Increase the speed of the drum beat, then slow it down, emphasizing that a strong movement can be done slowly.

Additional benefits

(a) The execution of strong movements can enhance awareness of the limbs.

(b) For children with a great deal of vitality, this activity can release a lot of energy.

(c) For those with behavioural problems, it can afford a harmless outlet for their anger or aggression. On occasion, it might encourage them to articulate their feelings verbally, giving you an insight into their problems.

(For further developments using strong movements for expression, see Section 5.).

More Demanding Movements
COGNITIVE DEVELOPMENT: SEQUENCING

AIM

To help children develop the ability to sequence, execute and remember a series of movements.

Movements

Establish a pulse or beat, and execute the movements in accordance with this. Gradually it will be possible to execute the movements in a definite rhythm (See Section 6). For example:

(a) ask the child to execute a simple movement: stand up from sitting;

(b) add another movement: turn around; execute the two movements consecutively;

(c) add a third movement: two jumps; execute all three movements;

(d) continue adding one movement at a time, until the child cannot remember any more. Gradually her ability to remember long sequences will increase.

Developments

(a) Ask the child to think of and execute movements of her own choice.

(b) In a group, ask each child in turn to suggest a movement, which is then added to previous ones.

More Demanding Movements
COGNITIVE DEVELOPMENT: COMPARISONS

AIM

To help the child become aware of differences and contrasts.

Movements

Game 1

Ask the child to do as you ask, and then, on a signal, to do the opposite. For example:

(a) they stand wide 'like a gate', then they stand narrow 'like a stick';

(b) they walk with large steps 'like a giant', then they walk with small steps 'like a mouse';

(c) they walk with strong steps, stamping the feet, then they creep quietly, without making any noise;

(d) they walk stretching up tall, on the toes, then they walk very low, with bent knees.

Game 2

Ask the child:

(a) to draw a small circle in the air in front of the body with her finger;

(b) to draw a larger circle in the air with her hand;

(c) to draw a larger circle still in the air with her arm;

(d) to draw a very large circle in the air, stretching up high on her toes, leaning far to the side, leaning down low to touch the floor, and then to the other side.

Variation

Draw circles in the same way to the side of the body, on the ceiling or on the floor.

Game 3

Blow up a round balloon, and slowly let it down again. Ask the child to imitate the balloon as it grows and shrinks. (See Section 5 for developments of this.)

More Demanding Movements
COGNITIVE DEVELOPMENT: SPEED

AIM

To further increase awareness of different speeds (see Section 2).

Movements

Ask the child:

(a) to walk slowly round the room;

(b) to stand and move her body slowly, in silence or to slow music;

(c) to execute slowly all the movements described in previous pages, for example, swings, turns, stretches;

(d) to repeat all the above, fast.

(For development of this into rhythm, see Section 6. For activities and movements to help increase understanding of abstract concepts, and of vocabulary, see group activities in Section 4.)

MOVEMENTS & ACTIVITIES FOR GROUPS

INTRODUCTION

Rayner (1971) stresses 'the importance of play as essential in acquiring serious skills'. It follows from this that children should be given ample opportunity to play as they grow up. Very young children play satisfactorily alone. As they grow older, they begin to play alongside other children, so it can be beneficial to take them to a playgroup once or twice a week where there are children of their own age. Gradually, children learn to relate to each other and to play together (Rayner, 1971). This stage of development can be helped along by activities such as those described in this section. The introduction of action songs which the children sing and execute together is also useful in helping them to become aware of each other, as well as being fun.

When a child has acquired some awareness of herself, the next stage of development is to gain recognition of others and their needs. From this, relationship skills will grow, and this increasing ability to engage in a relationship, and to communicate, helps a child's sense of her worth to continue to develop.

Activities described in this section are designed to be undertaken in groups. We begin with those which increase awareness of, and relationship to, others. Activities which continue to develop awareness of self, shape and space, and which strengthen the body are then outlined. Activities which help to develop cognitive skills and language are then described, and the section ends with a description of several folk-dances.

Group Movements
THE WORKING SPACE

There should be as few distractions such as books and toys as possible. Cover these with a cloth if necessary. It is advisable to use a room or hall which is large enough to allow some degree of free movement, but not so spacious that the children feel insecure, or run around wholly out of control.

Some children will immediately start to run around anyway, and there are several possible reasons for this:

◆ a need to let off steam after sitting for a long time;

◆ they are expressing their inner chaos;

◆ they are expressing their joy at sudden freedom;

◆ they are exploring the boundaries of the new space.

Possible ways to respond

1 Allow them to run around for a few minutes, then start your class.

2 Put on calming music, suggest a task which requires quietness, calmness and slowness.

3 'Ground' them (see Section 7, p139).

4 Stop them, and continue with your planned lesson (not recommended).

FOOTWEAR

The floor should be splinter-free, non-slip and not cold, and thus suitable for working in bare feet. This has the advantage that the children can feel the contact of their feet with the floor, thus increasing awareness of their feet as they touch it in a variety of ways. Also bare feet hurt less than even the softest shoe if they accidentally touch someone else's body.

USE OF SPACE

Working in a circle can be very beneficial for all. It gives a feeling of security and strength to all participants, and makes it easier to see and control the class. However, some children may not be comfortable with the strong feelings aroused when in a circle with others, and a few may be distressed by the constant eye contact. In this case, arrange the children in some other way:

◆ freely, allowing them to choose where to sit or stand ("Find a space. Twirl round with your arms out. If you touch anybody, you are too near. Move further away until you don't touch anyone.");

◆ in lines.

Young children have a tendency to drift towards each other when standing in a line or in their own space. When in a circle, most children tend to drift towards the centre, with the same result. Be alert to this, as it can lead to bumps and tears. As the children become more aware of their bodies and boundaries, this will cease to be a problem.

INSTRUCTION

Always demonstrate what you want by doing it yourself, while describing the movement at the same time. If children are unable or unwilling to copy, gently move them, 'feeding in' the experience of the movement, until they can do it themselves.

LESSON PLAN

It is a good idea to have in your head a lesson plan, even though you will probably modify or discard it. Be ready to change your plans at a moment's notice, according to what the children bring to the session: their feelings, what they tell you, toys. Decide on a solid structure of your own which does not change, but within which you can develop and change activities. For example:

Part 1   Ritual beginning: start with an activity which is the same every time. This enhances confidence and calms the children as they realize that they can do what is asked. For example: "Rise to tiptoe, stretch up and then shrink to the ground curled up."

Part 2   Necessitates paying attention. For example:

(a) Follow the leader. This can be done travelling around the room, if there are not more than 10–15 children. Ask the children to copy you as you execute movements appropriate to their ability. Over time you can increase the variety and difficulty of the tasks. Always try to introduce a rhythm. Gradually it will be possible to make this more interesting (see Section 6).

An example:

- ◆ 6 walks, stop with hands on head for 2 counts;

- ◆ 6 jumps, pause for 2 counts;

- ◆ 6 knee bends, stop with jump to feet apart and arms outstretched for 2 counts;

- ◆ Crawl for 6 counts, pause for 2 counts.

For larger numbers, either

stand in a circle so that all the children can see you, or let them choose a space and stand yourself where you can be seen, for example on a platform;

(b) Listen to a drum or music, and stop moving when it stops. This can be developed over a period of time.

For example:

- ◆ drum 8 even beats, stop;

- ◆ drum fast;

- ◆ drum slowly;

- ◆ drumming as above, ask the children to move only their arms, then only their legs, then bodies;

- ◆ ask the children to dance high or low;

- ◆ beat strong loud beats, and ask the children to use strong movements;

- ◆ beat softly, and ask the children to use gentle movements.

Gradually include combinations of fast and slow, then strong and weak.

(c) Ask the children

- ◆ to shake their hands in different positions in relation to their body: in front, at their sides, up, down;

- ◆ to shake different parts of their bodies: elbows, tummies, feet;

- ◆ to make other suggestions.

For further developments see Section 6

Part 3   Repetition of familiar material from previous session, to enhance self-confidence. Development of the familiar: for example, making small and large circles with the arms can be developed by asking the children to do so in front of the body, to the side, on the floor or on the ceiling.

Part 4   New material, new task in awareness of body, space, direction, weight or movement quality.

Part 5   Creative section. Encourage the children to be creative, imaginative, inventing their own movements. Develop this further. For example, ask the children how else they can make circles:

(a)   with the elbows, tummies, feet, knees;

(b)   by making cartwheels, turning on themselves, circling with others.

Part 6   Calming ending, with slow movements. For example:

(a)   stretch up slowly on the toes, opening the arms to the side; slowly go lower and lower until crouched on the ground, closing the arms across the body. Repeat three times;

(b)   sit on the floor; breathe deeply;

(c)   lie on the floor until touched: 'dead lions'.

Group Movements
SHADOWING & MIRRORING

AIMS

1 To further develop awareness of self.

2 To increase awareness of themselves in relation to others.

3 To teach children to look at others.

4 To help them acquire an appreciation of the movements of others;

Movement

Place one child behind another. Ask the front child to move her arms, legs or torso slowly, and encourage the child who is behind to 'shadow' (copy) her. Change them round.

You may find it easier, initially, to be the one who stands in front.

Development

(a) Place two children facing each other with hands touching, and proceed as above.

Some children may have difficulty with this because of a reluctance to make eye contact. Alternatively, they may relate to the other child by watching her limbs, thus avoiding eye contact.

Additional benefit

Visually impaired children will be able to follow and relate to another child, without the need to see her.

(b) Repeat (a) above, with hands about three inches apart.

Additional benefits

(a) Control, as the child learns to match her movements to those of others.

(b) Alertness as the child watches and copies others.

(c) Children who are reluctant to be close may so enjoy the activity that the amount of time they can face another person who is close to them may lengthen.

(d) As they copy and imitate, children are also expanding their movement repertoire and self-confidence.

Group Movements
SLIDING

AIM

To further increase awareness of the back as it maintains contact with the floor (see Section 2).

Movement

This was described in Section 2. Here the activity is the same, but is undertaken by two children. It is best to pair the children up with someone of a different size. This activity is therefore not reversible.

Ask the smaller child to lie on her back. The larger child holds her feet and, walking backwards, pulls her partner (gently) along the floor. **Only undertake this activity if there is enough difference in size and strength to enable one child to pull the other without risk of injury.**

Additional benefits

(a) The activity encourages caring and a sense of responsibility in the larger child.

(b) It encourages trust in the smaller one.

Group Movements
CONTROL

AIM

To enhance control and sense of self.

Movements

Game 1

Statues. Ask one child to make a solid shape, for example, supporting herself on both hands and feet on the floor. Ask another child to try and move her, push her or change her shape, being careful not to hurt her.

Additional benefits

(a) Increased self-awareness and strength in the solid child;

(b) Increased awareness of her own strength and how to use it in the pushing child.

Game 2

Grandmother's footsteps. This involves about 6 children. One child is 'grandmother'. She stands with her back to the others and a few feet away. The other children approach her slowly and carefully, without making a noise or being seen to move. 'Grandmother' turns her head from time to time. If she sees anyone moving, that person has to go back to the starting place again. The first person to reach 'grandmother' takes her place.

Group Movements
WEIGHT

AIMS

1 To increase awareness of, and strength in, the centre of the body, the stomach and back, thus enhancing sense of self.

2 To increase concentration.

3 To focus energy.

4 To increase awareness of the weight of the body, and of movements executed.

5 To foster determination.

Movement

Divide the group into pairs. Ask the children to sit back to back on the floor, with backs touching all the way down, and feet placed on the floor in front of them. Ask them to wriggle gently and to push their partner with their back.

Development

(a) Ask them to take it in turns, using their backs, to push their partner across the room. This can be controlled rhythmically. For example, count up to four while one child pushes, and then to four again as the other child does so.

(b) Ask them to try to push their partner across the room at the same time. **Ensure that the activity is playful and that no-one gets hurt.**

Additional benefits

(a) This activity requires and fosters more strength and also more self-esteem.

(b) It increases awareness of self.

(c) It is an activity which visually impaired children can execute in the same way as any other child.

Group Movements
ELASTICS

You will need:

lengths of elastic about 2 cm wide and 45 cm long, as described in Section 3, p54.

AIMS

1 To increase awareness of, and strength in, the arms and legs, through activities with a partner.

2 To enhance control of body strength.

3 To encourage elasticity and adaptability in the body.

Movements

Place one child's hand in one loop, and the hand of another child in the loop at the other end. Encourage them to move each others' hands and arms:

◆ lifting,

◆ lowering,

◆ circling,

◆ pulling away,

◆ moving towards each other,

◆ resisting in turn, then being passively moved by their partner.

Variations

Do the same activity with two elastics, one in each hand.
Do the same activity, with elastics attached to the toes or ankles.

Additional benefits

(a) The activity helps those children with poor muscle tone to increase muscular strength.

(b) It increases the ability to relate to, and to move with, a partner.

(c) It enables those who are reluctant to make physical contact to relate to others via the prop.

Group Movements
STRETCH LOOPS

Working with these allows free movement, requiring and enhancing control.

AIMS

1 To increase awareness of the centre of the body, and therefore of self.

2 To move with and relate to another person.

You will need:

two loops of stretch lycra, one about 3 metres long and 15 cm wide, made double, so that it is strong, the other, also made of double material and about 15 cm wide, but about 5 metres long.

Movements

1 Ask two children to step inside the shorter loop, and put it behind their backs. Invite them to lean back, pulling their partner with their bodies. If they are uncomfortable with this, place them outside the loop, holding it first with their hands, until their confidence grows. Encourage them to:

◆ take it in turns to pull each other across the room;

◆ pull at the same time;

◆ experiment, playing with the loop, moving each other around.

Supervise carefully, to ensure that no sudden pulling causes a child to fall over and be dragged across the floor.

Variations

Allow the children to face outwards, pulling with their stomachs. The children themselves may decide to pull with their arms. This will strengthen and increase awareness of the arms.

Additional benefits

Children who are uncomfortable with relating and eye contact can enjoy and benefit from this activity without the need to touch or look directly at their partner.

2 Ask from three to six children to step inside the longer loop and to lean back with their waists. Draw a circle on the floor. Play a game the aim of which is to pull the child on the opposite side of the circle into the centre.

3 Ask the children to hold the loop with outstretched arms. Start a simple dance, involving walking or galloping round in each direction, swaying and jumping.

Additional benefits

(a) The children learn to be aware of each other's changing needs, and to respond to them.

(b) Those children who resist proximity or eye contact will be able to join in a group activity without the need to touch others or too much closeness. They relate to the loop.

Group Movements
CLOTH

AIM

To increase awareness of, and relationship to, others.

Movements

1 Introduce the cloth by asking everyone present to sit round it, and to feel its texture. Describe it, or ask the children to do so.

2 With their feet underneath it, ask the children to make 'waves' as they kick their feet, or to shake it with their hands.

3 Ask them to lift it high on a given word or sound, and to see each other under it. Some may want to crawl under it to the other side. Let them. Make a game of it.

4 Ask one child to sit or lie in the centre of the cloth. Invite the other children to join you in holding the corners and sides. Encourage them to walk round in one direction, then the other. Although lifting the child on the cloth off the floor should be avoided, your assistance will probably be needed to help with sliding her weight.

Variation

Ask the children to pull the cloth across the room in one direction, and then the other, walking slowly, fast, or in any other safe way they can think of.

Additional benefits

(a) This activity stimulates turn taking as the children wait for their turn, and help to hold and move their peers in the cloth.

(b) It increases awareness of and strength in their hands and arms as they hold the cloth.

(c) It feeds in the experience of moving round, forward and back;

(d) It increases awareness of the back and hips by contact with the floor.

You will need:

for 5-6 children, a large piece of stretch lycra, or a curtain or sheet, about 2 metres square. For larger groups, a 'parachute' can be purchased (see Appendix II).

Group Movements
SEESAW

AIM

To develop strength in stomach and arms.

Movements

These activities are developments from those described in Section 1.

1 Two children sit on the floor holding hands, legs outstretched and slightly apart, the legs of one over those of the other. They rock backwards and forwards until lying down in turn. At first you may need to sit at their side, easing their descent with your hands behind their heads, so that they do not bump their heads as they lie down, and giving a feeling of security.

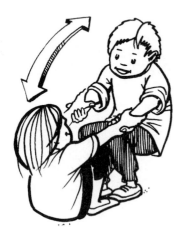

2 Two children sit on the floor, knees very bent, feet touching, holding hands. (Encourage them to hold each other's wrists rather than hands in this activity, as this is a firmer grip, and is less likely to slip.) In turn each leans back until lying on the floor, causing the other one to stand up. You may need at first to stand at their side with your hands on their backs, guiding and controlling them, and maybe helping them to stand.

Additional benefits

(a) The strength needed for these activities will be particularly beneficial to children with weak muscles, or those who are reluctant to move.

(b) These activities encourage eye contact.

(c) They encourage co-operation and social skills which are necessary for these tasks.

(d) The seesaw necessitates a rhythmic action, which is calming for all, and particularly helpful to those who have excess energy, or are over-anxious.

Group Movements
ROLLING

AIM

To increase awareness of the body as each part comes into contact with the floor, or with other bodies.

Movement

This is a development of 'Rolling' in Section 1. Ask the children to lie down on the floor with arms above their heads. Encourage them to roll along the floor. Ensure that they do not bump into each other.

Developments

(a) As the children approach each other, encourage them to gently roll over each other. This is an activity which can be greatly enjoyed. **Ensure that the children are considerate of each other.**

(b) Lay two children down on their stomachs, heads facing, with arms above their heads, holding hands. Help them to roll along the floor, maintaining the hand contact.

Additional benefits

(a) Increase of social skills.

(b) Co-ordination of movements with those of a partner.

(c) Consideration and gentleness.

AIM

To further increase awareness of body boundaries.

Movements

1 Two children make a bridge with their linked hands. The other children pass through the bridge under the arms.

Developments

(a) Two children make a bridge as above, but with their knees bent, forcing the other children also to go lower as they go through the bridge.

(b) As above, with the bridge going lower and lower until the children are kneeling on the floor.

(c) Half the children make arches on their hands and knees. The others crawl through the arches formed by their bodies.

(d) The carer sits on the floor, feet together, legs bent. The children wriggle under the arch formed by her legs.

In all the above cases, the child travelling through the arch or under the bridge will almost certainly touch the walls of the bridge or arch with some part of her body, thus increasing her awareness of the part which touches. She will also feel the contact of her body with the floor.

2 Distribute hoops around the floor. Play music and then stop suddenly. Ask the children to dance, then to stand in a hoop when the music stops, and to lift the hoop up their bodies until it is over their heads. They then put it down again and the game continues.

3 All the children except one stand next to each other, holding hands, with arms outstretched. One child zigzags through the arches formed by the arms. This activity is repeated, with the arches continuously made smaller, as the children move closer and closer together. If a child feels the moving child touch her body, she hums, or says "Bzzz". The object of the game is to get through the arches without causing the 'arch' to make a noise. The noise will help reinforce awareness of that part of the body which did touch the 'arch'.

Additional benefits

(a) All the children, even those standing still, become increasingly aware of their bodies.

(b) Social skills are enhanced, as the game depends on interaction.

(c) As awareness of body image increases, so will self-image and feelings of self-worth.

(d) For those who sometimes invade others' space, this game will increase awareness of body boundaries and of others' personal space.

Group Movements
SHAPE

AIMS

1 Further development of awareness and control of the body by making shapes with others. (See Section 3.)

2 Enhancing relationship skills by executing a common task.

Movements

1 Ask the children to sit and make a stone or rock: for example, a funny shaped one. Then ask them to make a funny shape with a partner, then with three children together. Encourage them to discuss the task and to find common solutions. Try to ensure that all have a say.

Development

Ask the stone to roll or to move across the room, maintaining its shape.

2 With children in pairs, ask one child to make a shape with her body and to hold the position. Ask the other child to (gently) change the shape by carefully moving the limbs and body of her partner.

Additional benefit

Increase of muscle tone as one child holds her position and the other exerts herself in trying to move her partner.

P

Group Movements
MOVEMENT IN SPACE

AIM

Increase further the awareness of the body and of its movement in space (see Section 3). The use of the scarf makes the movement visible, so that the child sees as well as experiences the movement.

Movements

Ask the children to hold the end of a scarf in one hand. Ask them:

1 to flick it up, raising their arms above their heads so that the scarf wafts upwards, then crouch down, bringing their arms down, until the scarf rests on the ground. Repeat this up/down movement several times;

2 to lift their arms above their heads standing with feet apart, then sway from side to side, lowering their arms to alternate sides, describing an arc over the head each time;

3 to sway from side to side, swinging their arms horizontally across in front of their bodies;

4 to turn on themselves, with arm outstretched, and watch the scarf drawing a circle around them;

5 to walk backwards (this is very difficult for some, who may require a hand on their shoulder and/or a hand round their waist to reassure them). Leaning forwards, shaking the scarf along the ground, they watch it 'wiggle like a worm'.

6 to find other ways of moving with the scarf:

◆ running, so that it flies out behind them;

◆ drawing 'S', '8', 'O', in the air with it, experimenting with size (when a shape or letter has been decided on, encourage the children to make it bigger, by moving their bodies as well as their arms);

◆ moving with the same qualities as the scarf: light, indirect, 'floating';

◆ pretending to fight each other with their scarves (why not – as long as you ensure that they avoid each others' faces);

◆ dancing with the scarves, alone and in pairs, to slow music with long phrases; then to fast and jolly music;

You will need:

one lightweight chiffon scarf for each child, about 75 cm long and 15 cm wide. Try to provide a variety of colours, so that each child can choose her favourite one.

◆ dressing up in the scarves and acting out the characters they feel they represent. (Ask them to suggest the sound accompaniment that they would like: for example, the sound of a drum, shaker or xylophone, or taped music which is slow, fast, happy or sad.)

Additional benefits

(a) Having a scarf often encourages children to move it when they may be reluctant to move themselves.

(b) The activity ensures that, by trying to move the scarf, they make larger movements than they might otherwise do. It is by making large strong movements that children are helped to become aware of their bodies.

(c) By seeing the quality of the movement of the scarves, the children are helped to become aware of qualities and to reproduce them in their own bodies.

(d) Some children are unaware of where they are in space. This type of activity can help to address this problem.

(e) Self-esteem will grow as the child sees her scarf move as a result of her actions.

(f) There will be increased awareness of space as the child sees the scarf moving through space in larger paths than her own limbs can execute.

(g) Creative play: some children may start to play imaginatively with the scarf, letting it become another character or an expression of their feelings.

(h) Some children who find it hard to relate to others may do so through their scarves.

Group Movements
DIRECTION

AIMS

1 Greater awareness of space.

2 Awareness of direction.

3 Increased ability of children to adapt to and control their environment.

Movements

1 Ask the children to, in turn, travel across the room:
- walking
- galloping
- jumping
- skipping
- hopping

Some children may find some of these movements difficult, as they require a level of development which in some children comes later than in others.

2 Ask the children to, in turn, walk, jump or hop backwards. This also requires a fair degree of development and self-confidence. Help a child who finds this difficult by holding her hand as she executes the task. Alternatively, encourage two children to hold both hands, one walking forward as the other walks backwards. Then change direction. Sing 'The Grand Old Duke of York' to accompany the movements.

For simple activities to develop awareness of the back, see Sections 1 and 2.

Additional benefit

Eye contact usually develops from this activity.

3 Help the child to walk sideways. This can be done in two ways.

(a) Step to the side with one leg, then close the other to it. Repeat across the room. When done fast, this can develop into gallops. For a child who finds this hard, face her, holding both her hands, and execute the task together.

'Feed in' the required movement with gentle pressure on her hands as you travel to the side and rise and descend with the movement. Encourage two children to hold hands and to gallop together.

(b) Step to the side, step across with the other leg, ensuring that the body does not turn.

4 Encourage her to make circles, using the different ways of moving listed above.

(a) Turn on herself on the spot;

(b) Move in a small circle on herself, gradually increasing the size of the circle;

(d) Move in a large circle with others.

Additional benefits

(a) Increased awareness of others, the speed of their movements, size of their steps.

(b) Social skills.

5 Zigzag

(a) Ask the children to move across the room in zigzags, alone, then in a line with the children following each other.

(b) An action game: sing 'Round and Round the Village'.

Ask all the children except one to stand in a circle holding ther hands high.

Verse 1: the child on the outside skips round the circle.

Verse 2: the children raise their arms, and she skips, zigzagging under them.

Verse 3: she stands in front of a chosen friend. Repeat the whole sequence with the chosen friend on the outside of the circle.

AIM

To help the children learn words through physically experiencing their meaning.

Movements

1 Over, through, round

Place some scarves on the floor, saying that they are 'puddles'. Ask the children to jump over the puddles, go round them or splash through them.

2 Behind, in front

Stand half the group dotted haphazardly around the room, and ask the others to walk in and out of them. On a given signal such as a drum beat, they have to stop behind another child. Repeat, but this time they have to stop in front of another child.

3 Round

(a) Ask one child to run round another child. Stress the word vocally as the child executes the task.

(b) Make a circle with half the children, and ask the others to run or dance round the circle, outside it, and then inside it.

4 Under

Ask the children standing in the circle to make arches with their arms, and ask the others to go through the arches, under the arms. (See 'Body boundaries' above.)

Group Movements

COGNITIVE DEVELOPMENT: MEMORY

AIM

To increase the child's ability to remember movements through use of the body

Movements

1 Stand the children in a circle. Ask one child to skip round in the circle and to stop in front of one of the others. Ask the child in the centre to execute a simple movement of her own choice. For example, she jumps and claps. The child she is standing opposite copies the movement, and then they do it together. They then change places, and the child who is now in the centre skips round and stops in front of another child. Repeat until all the children have had a turn.

2 Sequencing

(a) ask one child to execute a simple movement;

(b) all copy it;

(c) another child executes a simple movement;

(d) all copy it;

(e) all execute both movements consecutively;

(f) another child executes a simple movement;

(g) all copy it;

(h) all execute all three movements;

Continue adding one movement at a time until all the children have added theirs. As the children become more adept, it will be possible to stipulate that all movements must conform to a given rhythm: for example, four fast, two slow.

Additional benefits

(a) Increased attention.

(b) Social skills.

(c) Movement observation skills.

Group Movements
FOLK DANCING

Folk dances are great fun, and have many benefits.

1 They involve relationship skills, helping the children become aware of others as they dance with them.

2 Children develop increased awareness and use of space as they dance in prescribed patterns.

3 There is increased ability to remember sequences.

4 Children develop control as they become increasingly confident about starting and stopping and executing steps as required in conjunction with others.

5 Folk dances provide an opportunity for learning about a variety of cultures and countries. If you can find dances from the cultures of children in the class, their performance by the whole class will greatly enhance their feeling of pride in their culture. This will also familiarize other children with aspects of their classmates' lives of which they were previously unaware. Relatives and carers can be a rich source of information and support in this, often providing music and information on costumes, as well as helping to teach the dances.

There are many simple folk dances from all over the world. If you do not know any, or find existing ones too complicated, you can make up your own. Use any music in 4/4 time. Most English folk dance steps are skipped, but if skipping is not yet possible, they can be walked. This can develop to galloping and, finally, to skipping.

AN EXAMPLE OF A MADE-UP ENGLISH FOLK DANCE

Ask the children to stand in a circle and to hold hands.

(a) Walk or gallop seven steps to the left; change directions for one beat.

(b) Walk or gallop seven steps to the right.

(c) Go towards the centre for four counts, then out for four counts.

(d) Sway left, sway right, three claps.

Variations

Add jumps, turning on oneself, turning with a partner, or anything you or the children can think of.

A SRI LANKAN STICK DANCE

This can be simplified and adapted according to the ability of the children. Although traditionally danced with sticks, it is safer for young children to clap hands rather than to hold sticks. Use any music in 4/4 time, ideally from Sri Lanka.

Place the children in a circle, facing each other in pairs, some facing clockwise, their partner facing anti-clockwise. Count phrases of four counts. Ask the children to:

(a) Clap right hands with the partner, taking two counts.

(b) Clap left hands with the partner, taking two counts.

(c) Walk four paces to change places with their partner, one count per walk, to face each other again.

(d) Repeat the above sequence, (a) to (c).

(e) Repeat the above sequence, but instead of turning to face each other, the children move on in the direction they are facing until each child faces the next partner.

AN ITALIAN TARANTELLA

This is danced with a tambourine, sometimes shaking it and at other times beating it in time with the music in different positions. Using only skips and gallops, it can be danced in a number of ways, depending on the age and ability of the children. Here are some examples.

Ask the children to:

(a) Skip round the room, holding a tambourine in the right hand and shaking it above the head (16 counts).

(b) Turn to the right, leaning forward, shaking the tambourine near the floor, with the weight on the right foot, and pivoting on the toes of her left foot (eight counts). If this is too difficult, turn using tiny steps. Repeat to the left, with the tambourine in the left hand (eight counts).

(c) Stand with both arms above the head. Step to the right with the right foot, then close the left to it, beating the tambourine on the close. Repeat to the left, and then again to the right and left (eight counts).

(d) Lean down and, shaking the tambourine near the floor, run forward with small steps, gradually raising the tambourine up above the head (eight counts). With small steps, run backwards, gradually lowering the tambourine.

(e) Gallop round the room with big steps, beating or shaking the tambourine (16 counts).

As the children become more advanced, a section could be added where they beat each other's tambourines.

THE POLKA

This is danced in a number of European countries, including Poland, the former Czechoslovakia and Switzerland. Each country has its own national variations on the dance. Below is a description of a way to teach the basic step, gradually increasing the difficulty:

(a) The children face each other in pairs, holding both hands. As one moves her right foot, the other mirrors, moving her left foot. One child steps to the right with her right foot, then closes her left foot to it, and then steps right again lifting the left leg off the ground, holding for two counts. The other child mirrors this, executing the sequence on her other foot.

(b) As above, but add a hop on the left foot just before the first step to the right, and then a hop on the right foot just before stepping to the left.

(c) Repeat the whole sequence faster.

(d) The children now travel down the room, holding each other's waists, one forwards, one backwards, stepping diagonally rather than straight to the sides.

(e) Dancing alone, the children are asked to repeat the whole step, but adding a half-turn on the hop, thus executing a whole turn every two bars.

(f) Help the children to put their right hands on their partner's waist, and their left on her shoulder (thus bringing them closer together) and to travel down the room together, executing a half-turn on every hop, spinning round each other.

(g) When they can spin round each other, encourage them to travel round the room as they spin.

Physically impaired children can be involved in these dances. For example, they can be held in the arms of carers who dance, so that they gain the experience of bouncing up and down, or they can be pushed in their buggies, taking part in the circles, lines and other formations.

Visually impaired children can also take part in dances, particularly those which necessitate holding hands. They can be led by their sighted peers, and will eventually be able to dance unaided.

PERFORMANCE

Set dances can be executed for the enjoyment of the participants. They can also be performed to be watched by an audience, as can any other dance activities which evolve from improvisation and free dance. There are many benefits to be derived from performance, such as the following:

(a) the children's self-esteem, and pride in showing what they can do;

(b) control;

(c) motivation, as they work hard towards a goal.

However, there are also disadvantages. For example:

1   A greater degree of precision is needed than for a dance which is danced for fun. This requires more rehearsal, which can become boring.

2   Even when based entirely on the child's creative input, a performance needs to become more defined. This therefore leaves less room for a child to express herself. Constant repetition can result in total disappearance of the child's original expression and joy.

The advantages and disadvantages should be borne in mind and weighed up when planning a performance.

THEMES FOR CREATIVE MOVEMENT

INTRODUCTION

As children mature, they begin to want to determine for themselves how they are going to move, and to devise new ways of doing so. This:

◆ gives an alternative outlet for self-expression;

◆ releases frustration;

◆ stimulates their ability to think and move independently;

◆ encourages initiative.

Rayner (1971) stresses the importance of creative play. It is to be encouraged as it is the beginning of invention, later to be used by the artist and scientist alike. Most very young children need no encouragement in creative play. They copy activities which they have seen adults undertake. They make up stories. They may start with real objects or toys which represent real things, but they soon begin to use sticks, stones – anything which comes to hand.

As well as the wonderful array of toys available today, try to provide objects which are non-specific, for example plastic containers and saucepan lids, which can 'become' anything the child wishes.

Finally, as children develop, they are able to play with 'invisible', 'pretend' objects, in fact, they are able to mime anything and everything.

It is important for children not only to play together, but to learn to move together, as this develops their social and relationship skills. They measure their strength against that of their peers, and learn to balance and use their varying abilities, strengths and sizes, in a caring way.

When setting movement tasks, build in limitations, as this also encourages creativity. For example, ask the children to travel only by jumping, and ask them to think of lots of ways of doing so.

As discussed earlier, most young children enjoy enacting their favourite stories, songs or characters, and in fact find it easier to express themselves physically than with words. It will often be possible to evoke very creative and beautiful movements by taking stories and songs as a starting point. In this section, themes are proposed which lend themselves to creative movements: those which the children themselves can suggest and initiate.

Costumes are not essential, but are greatly enjoyed. It is not necessary to have a complete outfit: a hat here, a tail there, can help a child to imagine the whole, and to 'get into the part'. Start by suggesting themes which are within the experience of the children and are of interest to them. For example:

◆ animals,

◆ television characters;

◆ familiar songs and rhymes,

◆ simple stories which have been read to them.

Make up your own stories, alone or together with the children. They will soon begin to think up their own situations and initiate their own movements.

Physically impaired children could move their faces alone, or faces and arms, or, as suggested above, could be pushed or carried around.

Use any and every means to stimulate the children and to show them the myriad possibilities that exist. As outlined in the Introduction, use your voice, tell them stories, recite rhymes, sing them songs, show them photographs or pictures of animals. Use videos to demonstrate how an animal moves, or to tell a mimed or danced story which the children can then re-enact in their own way.

Every activity can be executed in a number of ways:

1. They can be simple mime or imitation of the animal or character.

2. They can be executed in unison with a partner or group, which can stimulate relationships and social interaction.

3. They can be performed rhythmically, with repetitions and pauses (see Section 6, 'Rhythm').

4. They can be danced to pre-recorded music, which can be used as a means of encouraging listening carefully to music. Ask the children to listen to the music, and to react accordingly: for example, following the tempo, dynamics, mood and quality of the music, and reproducing this in their movements.

5. Some of the children can dance and move, while others play simple instruments to accompany them.

Creative Movement
ANIMALS

Animals are usually much loved by children, and endless fun can be had 'being' or 'moving like' them. Small children may insist on 'being' cats or dogs. As they grow older, it will be possible to ask them to move 'like' a duck or tree, so that they become aware of what they are doing. Mention in passing, but do not insist on, appropriate movement qualities. For example, when they move like animals, confirm that horses gallop fast, that elephants are heavy, that mice scurry quickly in different directions.

Physically handicapped children can 'become' cats or dogs with their faces painted, perhaps arms too, or they can be pushed around fast like horses galloping, or in quickly changing directions like mice.

Gradually introduce less well-known animals by showing a video or photographs. Describe their shape, size, speed, and movement qualities, and encourage them to employ these. Stimulate them to make up their own animal dances, and to make up stories involving different creatures.

Creative Movement
BALLOONS

Movements

1 Blow up a balloon, and slowly let it down again. Ask the children to imitate the movement of the balloon as it grows and grows, and then shrinks again until it is tiny. Let them suggest different shapes: for example, a round one, a long thin one, one with curves, a twisty one.

2 Ask the children to float around lightly as a balloon does if held on a string.

3 Blow up a balloon as before, but this time let the air out suddenly, causing it to fly fast across the room. Ask the children to move in a similar way.

4 Prick the balloon, and show the children how the balloon falls to the ground. Ask them to pretend they are being 'popped'. **Do not actually prick the balloon unless you are sure that none of the children would be startled by the noise.**

5 Make up a story about a balloon. For example, it gets blown up, goes on a journey, gets lost, finds a friend, blows around with the friend, and so on.

Creative Movement
TOYS

Most children enjoy imitating their toys, or moving as they imagine they would move if they could. Either make up a story about toys coming to life or simply ask the children to move like balls, teddy bears, cars, puppets, robots, scarecrows, and anything else you or they can think of.

Creative Movement
WATER

This can inspire many different types of movement.

Movements

1 The sea

This activity is possible if the children have seen the sea or a film of it.

(a) Ask them to kneel, sit or stand, and move gently, like a calm sea.

(b) Tell them that the waves are getting bigger, and encourage them to move their bodies and arms more strongly, making larger movements.

(c) A storm: with your voice, or sound effects or music, stimulate them to move around the room with strong and fast movements.

2 Creatures who live in the sea

The children will probably start by crawling around on their stomachs, 'being' fish. Allow this and praise their endeavours. Use their activity to introduce the concept of floor patterns: for example, moving round in a circle, or across the floor.

Developments

(a) Encourage children's awareness of their classmates, and encourage them to move in relation to them, for example moving round someone else, or changing places with them.

(b) Gradually inspire them to move like a fish, a shark or a whale, or whatever they propose. Suggest that it may be easier to achieve the right quality of movement if they get up off their stomachs and onto their feet. It will then be possible to glide and float smoothly as fish do.

3 Mermaids

If they have seen the Walt Disney film of *The Little Mermaid*, they may be inspired to move like a mermaid, though very young ones may find it difficult to move as if they had a tail instead of two legs. For those who can, finding different ways of moving like a mermaid can be a very creative task. For example, they can get about by rolling, jumping (with their feet together) or sliding on their stomachs. They

can play ball as mermaids, reaching for it while keeping their feet together, and gently falling over into the water.

4 The Seaside

There are many seaside activities, for example:

(a) paddling;

(b) swimming;

(c) jumping waves;

(d) making sand castles;

(e) putting on suntan lotion;

(f) collecting shells or crabs;

(g) 'being' crabs.

Creative Movement
WEATHER

1 Raindrops

Using fingers, hands, then the whole body, the children represent raindrops gently or stormily dripping down the window pane.

2 Puddles and rain

For some children it may be necessary to put some mats or scarves on the floor to represent puddles. Others will be able to imagine them. There are many ways of moving in the rain. For example:

(a) jumping into puddles and getting splashed, or splashing someone else;

(b) jumping over puddles;

(c) running round puddles;

(d) running around in the rain, trying to keep dry under (pretend) umbrellas. **If real ones are used, great care must be taken to increase awareness of others to avoid injuries.**

(e) play 'Singin' in the Rain'. It is a very jolly piece, and has a strong repetitive rhythm which can inspire some rhythmic musical dancing.

3 Wind

Ask the children to imagine that they are being blown around by the wind on a windy day. Encourage them to 'be blown' forwards, backwards, sideways and round. Bang a drum and ask them to change direction on every beat.

Development (in pairs)

One child is the wind, the other is blown around by her. **Ensure that no touching occurs as this could hurt.** Help the 'blown' child to respond to the actions of the wind, to go in the direction indicated, to use the same movement quality as the wind, and to move the appropriate body part.

Additional benefit

Relationship skills are developed, as the child pays attention to the movements of the wind.

Creative Movement
WORK ACTIONS

Very young children may like to work with props at first. Others may feel quite happy working with 'pretend' tools.

Many work activities lend themselves to dances as they usually have an obvious pulse and rhythm. Others can be executed in a rhythmic way. For example:

1 Gardening

(a)   Digging and throwing the earth aside.

(b)   Pulling up weeds, moving along on each pull.

(c)   Watering, stopping to rub the sweat away or rub the back.

(d)   Executing two movements in the same sequence: for example, three digs and one back rub.

2 Vacuuming

By stressing the direction of the activity – forward, back, round – awareness of space can be enhanced.

3 Cooking

Pouring, weighing, stirring, pouring in ingredients, rolling, cutting.

4 Mining

'The Seven Dwarves' use a pickaxe for their work, swinging it down strongly in front of them, and lifting it up less energetically to the side, thus moving their arms in a circle.

5 Sawing wood

This can be done alone or with two children at either end of a saw, thus necessitating the need to work together.

6 Hammering nails (and hitting one's finger).

Creative Movement
CHARACTERS
INSPIRED BY MUSIC

Play music which suggests characters and situations: for example:

1) Debussy's 'Cakewalk'. Ask the children to improvise to it. Ask them what it reminds them of. Several groups have suggested 'Aliens'. Discuss aliens, how they look and how they move. Build up a repertoire of the children's ideas. Point out that some are bouncing, others grow and shrink, others do jerky movements, some do smooth movements, some are on the floor, some jump in the air.

2) Saint-Saën's 'Carnival of the Animals', particularly the slow tortoise, the heavy elephant, the jumping chicken and the quick birds.

Creative Movement
EMOTIONS

Feelings are a broad area which can be explored through movement and developed into dance, even with very young children. Ask them to move 'as if' happy, sad, frightened or angry. Older ones will then be able to tell you what happens to the body when they are experiencing these feelings. For example, a sad person's feet will feel heavy, they hang their heads and their shoulders, whereas an angry person may move sharply, with sudden starts and stops. Facial expression will also be involved.

Ask them to improvise a dance on a specific feeling. For example, invite them to show you the many different ways of expressing anger. These may include kicking, punching the air, stamping or jumping and landing heavily. **Always ensure that the anger is never aimed at a real person, and that no physical confrontation takes place.**

Use the sequencing game (see Section 3) to build up a dance, as in the following example.

1 One child stamps alternate feet three times. All copy.

2 Next child punches the air twice. All copy.

3 All execute first two movements consecutively.

4 Next child jumps, landing heavily, three times. All copy.

5 All execute all three movements consecutively.

Ensure that the children do not stand close enough to hurt each other.

Creative Movement
STORIES

Children love stories, and most will enjoy enacting those which have been read to them. Initially, choose simple ones which have plenty of action. Later it will be possible to add descriptions of mood or place which necessitate the children finding ways of moving which depict these. Other sections of the narrative may be best suited to mime. You can construct a dance drama, with dances to establish the characters and to describe their feelings, interspersed with sections based on mime or movements enlarged from natural action which advance the story.

Begin by telling the story and allowing the children to act out all the parts. Later it will be possible to allocate roles, then to introduce rhythm in those scenes which lend themselves to rhythmic movements, such as work actions. Some children may be able to accompany each other on simple instruments to a previously decided rhythm. Alternatively, you may prefer to choose suitable music (see Section 6).

Encourage the children to improvise their own interpretations. Try to use their ideas as much as possible. Encourage them not only to enact the narrative and portray the characters in it, but to think about movement qualities, shape, size and space. For example, 'The Gingerbread Man' gives an opportunity to think about shape, about how a biscuit or cookie in the shape of a man would move. He is not soft, so he cannot bend his knees or run in the ordinary way. Once you have made one or two suggestions as to how he could propel himself, the children will probably come up with many more. For example, he can

jump,

hop,

spin 180 degrees on each step,

sway from side to side.

The rhythmic element can always be introduced. The cooking actions of the Old Woman can be made into a rhythmic dance, and the qualities, shapes and speeds of the animals who chase the Gingerbread Man can be discussed and imitated.

Break down each story into separate scenes to facilitate the telling. For example:

◆ sad dance by Old Man and Old Woman,

◆ mime by Old Man who suggests cooking a Gingerbread Man,

◆ cooking dance,

◆ mime putting Gingerbread Man into the oven,

- Gingerbread Man runs away, chased by Old Man and Old Woman, but escapes,
- triumphant dance of Gingerbread Man,
- Gingerbread Man meets Cow, is chased by Cow, but escapes,
- triumphant dance of Gingerbread Man,
- Gingerbread Man meets Horse, is chased by Horse, but escapes,
- triumphant dance of Gingerbread Man, who is getting tired,
- Gingerbread Man meets Fox, is chased by Fox,
- Fox offers to take him across the river. Fox swims, Gingerbread Man behind him, then on his back, head, nose.

Very young children do not like sad endings and can be frightened by the idea of a hero being eaten. It may therefore be necessary either to let the Gingerbread Man escape being eaten or, if he is, to let him be coughed up again whole. For example, change the traditional ending, and let the Gingerbread Man trick the Fox into believing he is eating him, by holding a stick or cookie for him to eat instead. Alternatively, introduce the story with a cookery session in which you make Gingerbread Men together. Having eaten a delicious Gingerbread Man, few children will be upset by an animal eating one.

THREE LITTLE PIGS

This story gives opportunities for three work actions as each pig builds his house. The children can first discuss how to make a house of straw, wood or bricks, and you can help them break down each activity into several actions. For example, when building the house of straw,

> the straw is collected,
> tied into bundles,
> the bundles are piled on top of each other.

When making the house of wood,

> trees are chopped,
> wood is sawed,
> nails are hammered in.

The house of bricks is made by

> mixing mortar,
> laying it out,
> placing bricks on it,
> spreading more mortar on them,
> laying another row of bricks,
> putting windows and doors in,
> placing the roof on top.

All these movements lend themselves to rhythmic structure. The conversation of the wolf and the pigs which includes 'I'll huff and I'll puff' can be spoken by you, other children, or by the children who are portraying the wolf and pigs themselves. Children always enjoy the chase where the wolf tries to catch the pigs.

Creative Movement
FESTIVALS

Many festivals have stories which can be told through movement, music and mime. The benefits derived from depicting in movement stories from religious and cultural festivals include the following:

1 In schools where there is a wide cultural mix, this can aid acceptance and understanding between members of the different cultures, and can break down any potential prejudice before it is ever formed.

2 It can give children from ethnic minorities a deep sense of pride that their whole class are learning about and dancing stories which they have heard at home. Start by telling the story and describing the characters involved. Discuss with the children how they feel and how they would move.

THE CHRISTMAS STORY

The Christmas story gives opportunities for:

a tired dance by Joseph and Mary,
a lullaby dance by Mary,
dances for shepherds, kings, angels and the star,
dances of the animals in the manger.

THE HINDU DIWALI STORY

The Hindu Diwali story also lends itself to easy narrative:

a dance of the deer which Sita sees in the forest;
Sita's lonely dance when she is left alone in the forest;
a cautious hunting dance as Rama stalks the deer;
an aggressive dance by the monster Ravana and his followers, as he leads Sita away;
a happy dance by the monkeys as they build a path of stepping stones across the sea, which Rama crosses as he goes to rescue Sita;
a joyful dance with lights as Sita's return is celebrated.

PASSOVER

The story of this Jewish festival can be told by a series of simple scenes:

the Hebrew slaves work hard, carrying heavy rocks and stones;
Moses asks the Pharaoh to let his people go. Pharaoh refuses;
the slaves pick up their belongings and creep away;
they reach the sea; it parts;
they perform a happy dance as they reach the other side, and the sea closes behind them.

FIREWORKS

Holidays which are celebrated by letting off fireworks, such as 14 July in France and Independence Day in the USA, and, in the UK, Guy Fawkes Day, which celebrates a failed attempt to blow up the Houses of Parliament, also give opportunities for dance. You and the children can discuss the different ways fireworks move. They can execute their own dances, or you can help them make a group dance, moving in unison and in turn.

EASTER

Easter eggs can be hunted, picked up, put in baskets and then eaten. You can use real objects, or 'pretend' paper oval shapes, or simply use nothing and pretend to pick them up.

118

Early Movement Skills

© *Naomi Benari, 1999*
You may photocopy this page for administrative use only

Creative Movement
SPORT

For small children, a ball game is an obvious choice. It establishes clearly in the child's mind the actions involved in throwing and catching. It also helps children to concentrate and focus on more than one object at a time, in this case the ball and their hands.

Game

Put the children in a circle. Give one of them a ball and ask her to throw it to her neighbour. Continue until the ball has been all the way round. (Very young children could sit on the floor and roll it to each other.)

Developments

(a) Take the ball away, and ask the children to pretend to throw it round the circle.

(b) Suggest that they pretend to throw it high and to jump to catch it.

(c) Ask them to throw it low and to reach down for it.

(d) Suggest that they throw it to the side, forcing their neighbour to reach sideways for it (this may be suitable only for older children).

(e) Ask them to throw and catch it quickly.

(f) Ask them to throw and catch it very slowly.

(g) Ask them to catch it and then to turn around.

(h) Encourage them to find other ways of throwing it: for example, through their legs.

You could drum an accompaniment, or simply use your voice to encourage a rhythmic flow.

Creative Movement
ROBOTS

Many children find robots fascinating, and much fun can be had executing everyday activities, such as walking, turning, drinking and eating, in a mechanical way. Draw their attention to the strong, dynamic, rhythmic qualities. Point out that robots are made of metal, so they are stiff and strong. They can only move their joints with sudden jerky movements.

Movements

Start by suggesting movements to the children and ask them to take three jerks to complete each one. For example:

(a) raise one arm from the side of the body to above the head;

(b) lower it;

(c) raise the other arm;

(d) lower it;

(e) raise, then lower, both arms;

(f) swivel a quarter turn, swivel back;

(g) with one hand, pick up an imaginary cup, and take it to the lips;

(h) replace the cup (point out that the cup shape and size remain the same throughout);

(i) walking: lift one knee;
                stretch out the lower leg;
                put the foot down in front;
                repeat with the other leg.

(j) ask the children to improvise and to suggest other activities.

Creative Movement
SCARECROW

Scarecrows are filled with straw or another soft material. They move in a very floppy wobbly, indefinite way. For example:

1. Lift one arm and let it flop down to the side of the body. Repeat with the other arm;

2. Lift one leg, and let it flop down to the floor. Repeat with the other leg;

3. Walk with wobbly knees;

4. Flop the top half of the body down, and let the arms dangle.

Contrast the scarecrow with a robot, pointing out the differences.

Encourage the children to make up a story about robots and scarecrows. Accompany the robots on a drum, and the scarecrows on an instrument capable of more fluid sounds, such as a *Melodica*.

Creative Movement
CIRCUSES

For those children who have been to a circus or have seen one on video or television, this is a rich source of inspiration, as children usually love the humour of clowns and the expertise of acrobats and tightrope walkers, and love to imitate them.

CLOWNS

1 Allow the children to enact first what they have seen, such as the clowns walking into the ring and falling over (ensure that they fall carefully, without hurting themselves);

2 Add a rhythmic element, or accompany their falls with appropriate sounds, such as drum beats;

3 Help them to 'pretend to' bump into each other (carefully!);

4 Encourage them to throw and dodge imaginary custard pies;

5 Elicit further ideas for humorous activities.

Additional benefit

The further development of relationship and social skills.

TIGHTROPE WALKERS

1 Ask the children to walk along a real or imaginary thin line on the floor;

2 Ask them to imagine they are walking on a tightrope very high in the air. Suggest they might wobble;

3 Encourage them to:

walk forwards and backwards;

to swivel round and to walk the other way;

to bend their knees and to straighten them again;

to lift one leg and then to put it down.

Creative Movement
SHAPE

This activity has been described in Section 4. It allows for much fun and creativity, as the children explore shape.

Movements

1. Ask the children to sit and to make their bodies into:
   (a) the shape of a stone or a rock;
   (b) a funny shape;
   (c) a curved shape;
   (d) a shape with corners and straight lines.
   Repeat all the above in pairs, then in groups.

2. Encourage the children to make shapes that another child could crawl through, or (carefully) climb over;

3. Help them to draw shapes in the air:
   (a) a circle,
   (b) a square,
   (c) a triangle,
   (d) a funny shape.

4. Encourage them to walk in:
   (a) a circle,
   (b) a square,
   (c) a triangle.

5. Ask them to think up as many shapes as they can to make with their bodies in the air, and on the floor.

Creative Movement
DANCES

Some children may prefer to work in an abstract way. They can be helped to increase their creative skills by making up their own dances using everything they have learnt, as in the following examples.

1 They could combine walking, skipping, jumping, turning and hopping, in a variety of directions and levels.

2 They could contrast movement qualities, such as strong and gentle, and speeds such as fast and slow. The possibilities are endless. For example, older ones will be able:

(a)   to decide on a given rhythm and

(b)   to discuss relationships and floor patterns.

MUSIC
& RHYTHM

Music & Rhythm
MUSIC

Some carers may feel rather unsure about the choice of music for movement sessions. The aim of the following is to allay any fears in this regard, and to give ideas on the use of music.

It is true that music and movement tend to go together, and in some languages the same word is used for both. Yet they do not have to. Movement has a rhythm, a breath of its own, and can exist in its own right, creating its own rhythms, rather than following existing ones in a musical piece. Some of the best choreography has been created and performed in silence.

When encouraging children to move freely, making up their own dance, it is often preferable to let them move in silence rather than imposing an existing rhythm and sound. They themselves may then be able to suggest what type of music they would like played, or to play themselves on simple instruments.

When using music, choose that which supports and stimulates the quality, speed, mood and actions that you are aiming at.

RECORDED MUSIC

If you want to use music, and no accompanist or instrument is available, it is possible to use recorded music, although the wide choice of recordings available can be daunting. It is best to try and choose music without words, as words can be distracting if the child understands them, and frustrating if she does not.

PULSE

For music with a strong pulse, a good place to start looking is in the World Music department of any record store. Much Caribbean and African music has a strong beat, and most other countries also have music which is meant to be danced to. Much Latin American music has interesting rhythms, and is less emphatic, while having a definite beat.

CALMING MUSIC

Sometimes you may want music to calm the children down, or as an accompaniment to slow gentle movements. Start with your favourite music of this type. Alternatively, the slow movements of many symphonies or concertos are highly suitable. Children from any culture will almost certainly respond to the mood of this music. Alternatively, every culture has its own slow, calm music. All are eminently suitable.

Children can be very sensitive to the mood of music, and some may simply not respond if music is played which is not in tune with the way they are feeling. If working with tapes, keep a variety of different kinds of music (fast, slow, sharp, smooth, strong beat, no beat) readily available. As they get older, children can be asked what kind of music is needed for a dance, character, action, story or mood.

VOLUME

Be very aware of the child's needs. Most young children have very sensitive hearing and usually prefer music which is soft rather than loud. Some may put their hands over their ears if it is too loud, but others may simply withdraw and cease to pay attention to what is going on.

Children with a hearing impairment usually benefit from the boosting of the bass, as this is easier to hear. When working with a tape recorder, place the speakers on the floor, so that these children can feel the vibrations more easily. If using an instrument such as a piano or guitar, allow them to place a hand on it whenever they wish, as they will be able to feel the vibrations, and thus experience the rhythm, and sometimes the pitch, of the music.

TEMPO

Most music is recorded to be listened or danced to by adults. However, the heartbeat of children is faster than that of adults, and their legs are shorter. If you are asking the children to dance to recorded music, be aware that they may need music which is slightly faster than usual. This is not such a problem, as it is now possible to buy tape recorders which play at varying speeds. (See Appendix II for a supplier.)

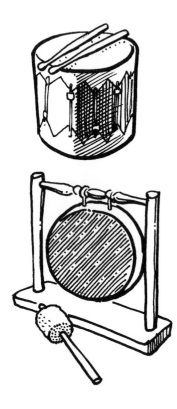

PERCUSSION INSTRUMENTS

It is not necessary to be a musician to use simple percussion instruments, such as drums, wood blocks or even castanets. These can be employed to establish a pulse, or to emphasize a strong movement. It is best to choose small instruments that you can hold and play while paying full attention to the child or class.

MUSIC APPRECIATION

This can be enhanced from the earliest age, in several ways.

1 Ask the children to dance to music which is slow and calm. If they do not move appropriately, tell them that it is slow and calm, and ask them to find movements which go with it.

2 Repeat, with music which is

fast,

slow,

strong,

gentle,

and which encompasses all the above.

Ask the children to dance, while letting the music tell them how to move. Point out to them the pauses, and differences in dynamics, tempo and rhythm.

3 Play music, and ask them how it makes them feel: for example, happy, sad, tired or angry. Ask them to do a sad, tired or angry dance. Then discuss the quality, size and shape of movements which they used.

4 Play music, and ask the children who it reminds them of: for example, a giant or a mouse. Ask them to move appropriately.

5 Play music from a variety of cultures and countries. Use the opportunity to tell the children something about them: for example, whether it is hot or cold there, and what people there like eating.

Development

Either tell the children a story, or ask them to help you to do so, and invite their co-operation in deciding what kind of music should accompany each mood, character or event. Either play appropriate music on an instrument, find something suitable on tape or ask the children themselves to accompany the movements on simple instruments.

PHRASING

From the earliest stages of development, children will respond to movement tasks which are requested in the form of a phrase, even when there is no music: for example, "stand up, turn around, stretch up" (with your voice going up on 'up'), "sit down"(voice coming down on 'down'). This gives a feeling of wholeness, as well as increasing self-esteem, as the child realizes that she has completed a task.

Music & Rhythm
RHYTHM

An ability to move rhythmically has advantages for all children. For example, it can calm a child, giving a sense of predictability and security, and it can enhance self-esteem, as a child realizes that she can move in time with a given definite rhythm.

For children with a hearing impairment, the acquisition of the ability to move rhythmically can be of particular benefit. As they learn to feel rhythm inside their bodies, they will be able eventually to dance rhythmically, alone and with each other, without the need to rely on the music or a hearing person.

ACTIVITIES

1 Ask the children to sit and clap fast, then slow, to familiarize them with the fact that music and rhythm can be fast or slow. Get them to move their bodies as they clap, for example leaning far to each side as they clap slowly on the floor, then sitting straight as they clap fast. This helps them to remember the rhythm with their bodies, in relation to the spatial pattern they are creating.

2 Ask the children to clap strongly (loudly) then gently (softly).

Developments

Ask the children to clap:

> fast and loudly,
> slowly and quietly,
> fast and quietly,
> slowly and loudly.

3 Repeat (1) and (2) and the developments, using simple percussion instruments, such as wooden sticks or drums.

4 Pauses or rests. Introduce pauses, telling the children to hold their hands out in front of them on the pause. Saying "stop" often helps. Try to avoid counting. For example, do not say "One, two, stop" but rather, "clap, clap, stop", as young children who cannot yet count may feel intimidated. Children who cannot count up to two are capable of clapping or playing intricate rhythms, because they feel them in their bodies. For example:

clap, clap, stop;
clap, clap, clap, stop.

Children with a hearing impairment often benefit from having the rhythm first clapped on their hand or chest by a hearing adult so they can feel it, and will thus know what is required.

Older children may be capable of more intricate rhythms, using fast and slow together. For example:

two slow, three fast, stop;
three fast, two slow.

Developments

Combine strong and weak beats in one phrase:

strong, weak, strong, weak;
weak, weak, strong, stop.

5 Invent other rhythms of your own, or ask the children to do so, and to copy each other.

6 Combine fast, slow, weak and strong. For example:
one slow weak, stop, three fast weak, one slow strong.

MOVING RHYTHMICALLY

When the children are able to clap or beat a simple rhythm, ask them to stand up and to move in the same rhythm. For example:

three slow jumps, stop;
moving in other ways to the same rhythm, or thinking of variations, such as three walks, stop;
three claps, stop. Then sing and dance "With your hands you clap, clap, clap".

Developments

(a) Ask the children to find a partner, and to move with them holding both hands in performing the above activities. This helps those who are more able to help those who are less so, as it can be uncomfortable to jump up and down, or to walk or turn, at a different speed from that of a partner. Also the less able will be able to feel the rhythm of their partner.

(b) In pairs, ask one child to clap a rhythm and the other to move to it. For example, one child claps three slow, stop; the other child watches, and does three jumps, stop, or any other movement you or they choose.

(c) Set simple rhythms using fast and slow beats and pauses, loud and soft sounds, and ask the children to improvise their own dances.

Music & Rhythm
MUSIC YOU MAY FIND USEFUL

For Rhythmic Movements

◆ Pop music of today.
◆ Pop music of yesterday, such as for the Charleston, rock 'n' roll, the Twist.
◆ World music from:

Africa	Middle East
British Isles	South America
Eastern Europe	Sri Lanka
India	West Indies

For Slow, Calm Movements

◆ Slow movements from:
Tchaikovsky's violin concerto
Bruch's violin concerto
Mendelssohn's violin concerto
Mozart's horn, clarinet and oboe concerti
◆ Some Indian Ragas
◆ World Music

For Work Movements

◆ 'Hey Ho, Hey Ho, it's off to work we go', *Snow White*, Walt Disney

For Witches, Wizards

◆ 'In the Hall of the Mountain King', *Peer Gynt Suite*, Grieg
◆ *The Sorcerer's Apprentice*, Dukas

For Animals

◆ *Carnival of the Animals*, Saint-Saëns

For Sea or Space Themes

◆ Mood or techno music
◆ *The Engulfed Cathedral*, Debussy

For Rain

◆ 'Singin' in the Rain'

◆ Familiar songs and nursery rhymes

ADDRESSING SPECIFIC PROBLEMS

SECTION 7

INTRODUCTION

A child's behaviour or physical condition may lead you to suspect that she would benefit from expert help. In the UK state system, appropriate channels for assessment, referral and treatment are usually available. Other countries will have their own assessment routes. For physical problems, consult a family doctor, osteopath or physiotherapist.

Discuss suspected emotional problems with the child's teachers, who will almost certainly suggest therapy if they feel it would be appropriate. Therapy for emotional problems can take a number of forms. For example:

- play therapy, in which the therapist observes the child playing, and from this draws conclusions as to the cause of her problems and the best way to address them;
- behavioural modification, where acceptable behaviour is praised, and unacceptable conduct is ignored;
- family therapy, where the whole family sees the therapist together to find new ways of relating within the family.

In some parts of the UK, therapies in a variety of art forms are also available. These include drama, art, music, movement and dance. Addresses of UK organizations which provide these are given in Appendix II.

Practitioners in these disciplines work in a variety of ways.

1 Some start by allowing the child to express herself freely in art form. According to what they learn from this, they are then able to address the problem itself, by looking at the emotions causing the difficulty.

2 Others will try to modify the expression, the picture, movement, or music.

3 Where possible, some may prefer to talk with the child about the game, picture, dance or music which she has produced. This increases realization in the child herself of the issues involved. This of course depends on the verbal skills and maturity of the child.

4 Some may use role play, employing themes suggested by the child or by themselves.

5 Some therapists believe in a totally non-directive approach, while others believe in controlling the sessions.

Whether or not a child receives therapy elsewhere, there are a number of ways in which you may wish to address specific problems when you encounter them. These are described below. However, it is advisable to approach every child holistically, that is, to see each one as an individual, for whom the behaviour, needs and feelings are part of the whole person.

Assume that the child has a reason for behaving the way she does. Accept her and her actions totally and respect her choices. Create situations whereby she herself will want to modify her behaviour. In movement sessions, help her to do so gradually, increasing first the choice of strength of movements, then the speed, then the space used. Make everything you do into a game which she wants to play.

Allow yourself to be led throughout by the child. Be sensitive to her non-verbal communication. Try to create an atmosphere of security, where the child feels safe. Give continuous encouragement.

Soft play areas, cushions and climbing apparatus are very useful, and are usually greatly enjoyed by children (see Appendix II for addresses of UK suppliers). However, whenever possible, use your own body as a support, and as something to climb over, pull and push against, because (a) you are more sensitive than an inanimate object, and (b) this will increase the child's ability to interact and trust.

No labels have been used, as it is more important to be aware of behaviour itself, rather than affixing labels or names to the difficulties. As stated above, if a serious condition is suspected, seek expert advice.

Some children run away, for a variety of reasons:

1 Attention seeking. After ensuring that they cannot leave the room or hurt themselves or others in any way, ignore them, praise others and introduce an activity which causes laughter and pleasure. They usually return.

2 They cannot cope with the group's proximity, noise or eye contact. Allow them to participate at a distance, or arrange the children in a straight line, or in such a way that they are all scattered around the room facing you.

3 They are very active and energetic.

(a) Start with movements which use the child's quality and speed. Gradually modify these, decreasing energy level and tempo until the movements are slow and calm.

(b) Play slow, calming music. Speaking quietly and slowly, set a task requiring slow, gentle movements.

(c) Help them to develop self-control through movement games:

> let them run until you shout "Stop!";

> let them run until they themselves shout "Stop!";

> musical statues: run, walk or dance, and freeze when the music stops;

> musical bumps: sit on the floor when the music stops.

(d) Help them develop rhythmic movements, such as walking or jumping to a given rhythm: for example, two slow, three fast, pause.

(e) Praise and reassure constantly as this enhances self-esteem and reduces anxiety which can often show itself as excitability.

(f) Increase concentration through movement games.

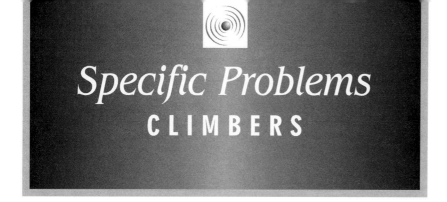

Specific Problems
CLIMBERS

Some children make for the highest ledge as soon as they enter a room. Accept their need and start where they are.

1. Put on rhythmic music, and stand and dance as near to the child as she will tolerate.

2. Tap a rhythm gently on her legs, or gently move her legs or feet. Stop immediately if this is resisted.

3. Hold her, with her arms around your shoulders and her legs around your waist. If she does not hold on, try to hold her anyway. Alternatively, carry her on your back, as this is less of a strain. Dance.

4. 'Ground' her. This can help to calm her down, raise her self-confidence, and help her to acquire balance. Make it fun to be on the floor. For example:

   (a) With the child's back to you, hold her firmly around the waist. Stop her running, or lift her down from the ledge, and swing her round. This is usually greatly enjoyed. Then lower her to the floor.

   (b) Sit her down, sit behind her and rock with her side to side, then forward and back. Talk or sing throughout to reinforce feelings of confidence.

   (c) Lay her down, and gently roll her:
   slightly away from you, and back again;
   onto her side and back again;
   onto her tummy and on to her back again, facing in the same direction. Talk or sing throughout.

   (d) Lay her down, hold her by her feet, and tell her what you would like to do. Then gently drag her around the room. Sing and smile throughout. This is usually greatly enjoyed. Stop immediately if it is not.

   (e) Sing 'Incy, wincy, spider', allowing her to climb on the words describing the spider's ascent. On 'Down came the rain and washed the spider out', allow her to jump or climb down. This game accepts her chosen behaviour, while putting it in a controlled framework. (In other situations, this song is used to enhance fine motor control, using hand movements only.)

   (f) 'Humpty Dumpty'. Sit on the floor and sway. On 'fall', ask her to roll onto her side or back.

   (g) Suggest activities and games which necessitate being on the floor. For example, being sea lions, lizards or snakes.

Specific Problems
CHILDREN WITH LITTLE SENSE OF SELF, LITTLE BODY AWARENESS

You will need:

a standing mirror,
preferably one which tilts

Imitate and reflect every movement the child makes, however small. This helps her to realize that what she does is accepted. This can be done in silence, or you can comment verbally on what she and you are doing.

Over the weeks, most children will allow you to move nearer as you copy them. However, as soon as they show any discomfort, move away and continue reflecting. They may begin to control you, making you jump and turn, and laughing as they realize their power.

ACTIVITIES

1 Place a mirror in the centre of the room, and draw the child's attention to it. Allow her to spend some time looking into it. She may make faces at herself. Put her hand on it and take it away again.

2 Slowly tilt or move the mirror so that her reflection moves.

3 Move it away from her, encouraging her to follow.

4 Stand next to her, or behind her, and move and dance, so that she sees your reflection move.

5 From behind, hold her around the waist, and gently sway her from side to side. Hold her hand or hands, and gently move them up and down, side to side, forward and back. Encourage her to dance.

See Sections 1, 2 and 3 for other ideas on improving body awareness.

Start gently, gradually building up contact, moving on to the next activity only when the previous one has been accepted. For example:

1 If the child is sitting, sit next to her, making no demands or other contact. If she is lying down, lie next to her. Look at her from time to time.

2 Sit behind her with your legs apart, and cradle her against your body, and then rock from side to side. Sing 'Row the Boat' as you rock.

3 If she is lying down, pick up her feet, and move them slowly and gently. Do not force eye contact if she does not want it.

4 Slowly and gently pull her along the floor by her ankles, talking or singing as you do so.

5 Monkeys: Kneel in front of the standing child. Encourage her to put her hands around your neck and her legs around your waist. Put your hands on the floor, and begin to crawl. Encourage her to grip very firmly. (Ability to do so is a sign of willingness to be involved.)

6 Kneel in front of her with your back to her, and encourage her to hold you round the neck. (You may need the help of another adult in this.) Gently lean forward until you are on your hands and knees. Sway gently forward and back, and then start to crawl. The child may want to continue leaning on you, or may prefer to sit upright.

7 If she is sitting, sit facing her, hold her hand, and rock backwards and forwards. Sing 'Seesaw' as you rock.

All the above activities can be executed by two children after the child has lost her anxiety about executing them with an adult. Ensure that the supporting child is large and strong enough to do so, and stay near them, helping if necessary.

S E C T I O N 7

141

You will need:

lengths of elastic,
about 45 cm long and
2 cm wide, with loops
at each end

Some children will resist touch. **Be very alert to their needs, and never force your touch if they appear distressed by it.**

AIM

Encouraging and helping the child to move, without the need to touch her.

Movements

1 Ask the child to hold one end of the elastic, or gently place it around her finger or wrist. Gently move her arm by moving the other end of the elastic. Repeat with the other hand, and then the feet. Encourage her to move you in the same way.

Additional benefits

(a) The child relates to you without the need for touch.

(b) She experiences moving passively.

(c) Increase of muscle strength.

2 Introduce games, such as rough and tumble from time to time, but only continue if they are genuinely enjoyed.

3 Offer the child an attractive toy, which she can only have if she comes and takes it from your hand.

4 Pretend that you cannot get up from the floor, and ask for her help.

5 Play games which involve going under, over and round another person. Accidental touch will result.

See Sections 3 and 4 for other ideas on touch.

Specific Problems
LETHARGIC CHILDREN

Some children often need strong motivation and stimulation to be persuaded to move. Start where the child is. Find out what interests her, and try to relate a movement game to this interest. Sometimes a song or rhyme on a relevant subject is enough. If you do not know one, make one up.

Movements

1. Move the child, to 'feed in' the experience of moving. For example:

    (a) roll her along the floor;

    (b) slide her along the floor on her back, holding her feet, in a straight line, round the room, zigzag;

    (c) standing or sitting, holding hands, sway and dance to music;

    (d) sitting behind her, holding her shoulders, sway her from side to side, singing or reciting a favourite song or rhyme.

2. Play with the cloth. Throw it up and down, occasionally letting it land on her arm or leg, being careful not to cover her face. Encourage her to kick or push it off. Be ready to stop immediately if she shows signs of not enjoying the game.

3. Throw or roll a ball to her, and encourage her to throw or roll it back.

4. Encourage her to move her arms holding a scarf, up and down, from side to side, round in a circle – any way she chooses. Small movements will be amplified by the scarf.

Additional benefit

(a) The scarf gives a visual confirmation of the result of the movement, reinforcing the physical sensation.

(b) Increased self-esteem at the clear evidence of the result of having made the effort.

You will need:

a cloth about 2 metres square
a soft ball about 30 cm in diameter (very small children may find it easier to catch a ball which has a net around it)
a scarf

SECTION 7

Specific Problems
CHILDREN WITH LOW MUSCLE TONE

This condition is sometimes linked to a wider problem. Expert advice should be sought to verify its cause and to seek appropriate treatment.

Described below are some movement activities which can help to strengthen muscles.

1 With a partner, seesaw. Sit the children on the floor facing each other, with legs out in front of them, the legs of one over those of the other. Encourage the children to lie down on the floor as they rock backwards, and to pull their partner up after she has lain down.

2 Standing up. Ask the children to sit on the floor facing each other, holding hands, with feet on the floor, and knees very bent. Encourage them to pull on each other's arms as they straighten their legs in an effort to stand up at the same time.

3 Seesaw to standing up. As (2), but one child starts standing up. As the other child pulls in order to stand up, the other sits down. Reverse.

4 Sit the children on the floor back to back, backs touching all the way down. Ask them to take turns to push their partner around the room by walking their feet along the floor.

5 As (4), but ask them to push simultaneously, seeing who can push further. Be sure that they are of roughly similar weight.

6 Stand the children up. Ask them to hold hands and to pull away from each other, making interesting shapes.

Additional benefit

These movement activities not only help to strengthen muscles in limbs and stomachs, but also help children become aware of their tummy and chest. This leads to increased self-awareness and self-esteem.

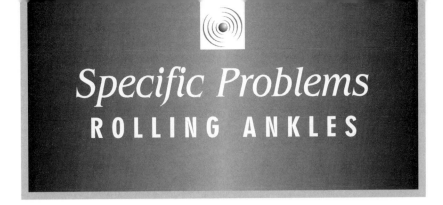

This condition can be caused by the wearing of nappies/diapers, and will usually disappear when these are no longer needed. However, it could be caused by a misalignment of the hips or a problem in the knee, and it is best to get specialist advice from a physiotherapist or an osteopath.

Arch supports are sometimes recommended. These correct the symptoms, and train the foot to hold itself correctly. However, the use of these is not sufficient, as there is a danger that the muscles will become lazy, relying unduly on the supports. Exercises to strengthen the muscles on the inside of the ankle, and under the arch are also needed. A few are described below. Repeat each exercise several times, two or three times a day, sitting on the floor.

1. With the child sitting with legs outstretched, ask her to make the soles of her feet 'look at each other'

    (a) with feet relaxed,

    (b) with toes pointed to the floor,

    (c) with toes turned up to the ceiling.

    Ask her to make circles with the feet, first in one direction, then the other. If the child cannot do this alone, gently hold her feet and help her, so that she can experience the movement.

2. With knees bent and feet planted firmly on the floor, ask her to make the soles of her feet 'look at each other'. Do not allow the knees to bend outwards too much.

AIMS

To help the child become aware of her body through contact with the floor.
To increase eye contact.

Movements

1   As the child lies on the floor, hold her ankles and gently pull her along. Look at her to measure her reaction, and be prepared to stop immediately if she is not happy. Avoid direct eye contact lasting for more than a split second. Look away before she does, and then back again, until she is happy with looking at you.

Additional benefit

This 'feeds in' the sensation of moving in different ways through space: backwards, in a circle or zigzag.

2   'Cloth game'. Ask the child to sit or lie on a cloth. This should be about 2 metres square, either made of stretch lycra or a simple piece of cloth such as an old curtain.) Slowly at first, drag her around the room. Maintain eye contact as in activity 1. (For expansion of this in a group, see Section 4.)

3   'Ball game'. Lie on your front on the floor and ask the child to do the same. Roll a ball to each other.

See Sections 1 and 2 for activities which involve eye contact.

Specific Problems
RELUCTANCE TO TALK

Movement can create a surge of energy and emotion, which can lead to talking. Never ask the child to make a sound, or express disappointment if she does not. You may want to try to find out the possible cause of her silence. There are many, including the following:

1 Anger: encourage her to express this physically.

   (a) Initiate actions and movement games which entail movements which are aggressive, outward, and straight, such as punching and kicking (ensuring that there is no recipient). Strong movements may evince sounds such as grunts. Comment verbally but non-judgementally on what she is doing.

   (b) Suggest that she move like a tiger who stalks, then suddenly pounces on her prey. As you demonstrate and suggest, use sounds to amplify the movements.

2 Lack of trust and fear of making mistakes: this sometimes happens with children who speak another language at home, and do not feel confident in English.

Activities

1 Breathe in slowly and out fast.

Variation

Add stretching slowly up during inhalation and touching the floor fast while exhaling. The sudden movement with the exhalation sometimes induces an involuntary sound. It is then more possible to elicit other sounds.

2 Games. Introduce games which are funny and so entail laughter, or those which rely on vocal sounds. Here are a few examples:

1 Run, 'stop'.

Ask the child to run around, and to stop when you shout "stop". Ask her to try to stop you running by shouting "stop" or any other sound. This game is often more effective if played in a group (see Section 4), as the desire to control peers and to take turns can be irresistible.

2 Buzz

In a group, ask the children to stand holding hands, with arms outstretched. Encourage another child to zigzag under the arms. Gradually make the line tighter by moving the children nearer to each other, so that it becomes impossible to go under the arms without touching the other children. Tell them to 'buzz' or hum when they are touched.

3 Tunnels

Ask each child to make a tunnel with her body, on hands and feet, gradually going lower and lower. One child goes under the tunnels, causing them to 'buzz' when touched. Take turns.

4 Hello Song

Make up a song, naming each child in turn, and ask them to join in. For example: 'Hello Amy, how are you? Hello everyone, I'm OK'.

Specific Problems
EMOTIONAL &
BEHAVIOURAL DISORDERS

There are a wide variety of causes of emotional and behavioural disorder, and these can show themselves in many ways. Start by accepting totally the child's mood and movement qualities. Encourage her to express herself physically, through movement and dance. Ask her to show you how she feels. Allow her to chose her own music, to tell you what kind of music she would like. Encourage her to 'be' or to 'move like' anything or anyone of her choice.

This expression of the child's feelings may temporarily make her feel better, but in isolation is unlikely to help long-term. Observe her movements and try over the weeks to increase the variety of movements and to modify them gradually. Help her to execute movements which are both strong and gentle, fast and slow, straight and curved, indefinite and rhythmic.

After dancing for a while, those who are articulate may be able to talk about how they feel.

CONCLUSION

CONCLUSION

In the preceding pages it has been shown that movement and dance can not only increase co-ordination, strength, poise and balance, but can also do much more in increasing emotional well being and cognitive skills. Movement and dance can:

1 help children gain self-confidence as they master their bodies; this self-assurance can then facilitate learning in all other areas;

2 help children learn about themselves and the world around them;

3 provide an alternative means of expression for those who have not yet learnt to express themselves verbally;

4 together with song, enhance children's speech and language;

5 together with music and rhythm, help to improve numeracy;

6 help children to relate to others and increase social skills.

It has also been suggested that creative play is important in the development of a child's creative thinking. In the UK there is a big drive towards increasing the literacy and numeracy of pre-school children, and it would be a great shame if, in pursuing these goals, some of the tools which could help in achieving them were to be forgotten.

In reducing movement, music and play in children's experience, we would also be impoverishing their lives.

APPENDIX I

Words of Songs and Rhymes

By first lines alphabetically, by Sections

Section 1

A lady goes a-trot, a-trot, a-trot, a-trot
Then she goes a-gallop, a-gallop, a-gallop, a-gallop
And then she goes a-canter, a-canter, a-canter, a-canter
Then she goes hobbledy, hobbledy, hobbledy, hobbledy
And falls down a big black hole.

Ride a cock horse to Banbury Cross
To see a fine lady on a white horse.
Rings on her fingers and bells on her toes,
She shall have music wherever she goes.

Round and round the garden like a teddy bear,
One step, two step, tickly under there.

Row, row, row the boat
Gently down the stream,
Merrily, merrily, merrily, merrily
Life is but a dream.
Row, row, row the boat
gently down the stream,
If you see a crocodile
Don't forget to scream.

This little piggy went to market,
This little piggy stayed at home.
This little piggy had roast beef,
And this little piggy had none.
And this little piggy went 'wee wee wee' all the way home.

Seesaw Margery Daw,
Jenny (use the child's name) shall have a new master.
She shall have but a penny a day
Because she can't work any faster.

Section 2

Clap hands, Daddy come home,
Daddy bring a cakey home
For his little Mary (use the child's name).

Five little monkeys jumping on a bed
One fell off and he bumped his head
mother called the doctor and this is what he said

'No more monkeys jumping on the bed.'
Four little monkeys …
Three …

Mulberry Bush (The carer can suggest any movement or activity)
Chorus:
Here we go round the mulberry bush, the mulberry bush, the mulberry bush
Here we go round the mulberry bush, on a cold and frosty morning.
Verse:
This is the way we wash our face (hands, clean our teeth, stamp our feet, jump up and down, turn around, etc)

One finger, one thumb keep moving (× 3)
We'll all be happy and bright.
One finger, one thumb, one arm keep moving (× 3)
We'll all be merry and bright.
One finger, one thumb, one arm, one leg keep moving (× 3)
We'll all be merry and bright.
One finger, one thumb, one arm, one leg, stand up, sit down keep moving (× 3)
We'll all be merry and bright.

Two little dicky birds sitting on a wall,
One named Peter, one named Paul.
Fly away Peter, fly away Paul
Come back Peter, come back Paul.

Twinkle, twinkle, little star,
How I wonder what you are,
Up above the world so high,
Like a diamond in the sky.

We are the music men and we come from music land
And we can play
What can you play?
We can play the piano, piano, piano
We can play the piano, pia piano.
We are the music men and we come from music land
And we can play
What can you play?
We can play the triangle, triangle, triangle
We can play the triangle, tria triangle.
(drum, flute, trombone)

Section 3

Five little ducks went swimming one day
Over the hills and far away.
Mother Duck said 'Quack quack quack quack'
And only four little ducks came back.
Four little ducks …
Three little ducks …
Two little ducks …
One little duck …
Mother duck went swimming one day
Over the hills and far away
Mother Duck said 'Quack, quack quack quack'
And all the little ducks came swimming back.

Section 4

Round and round the village (× 3)
As you have done before.
In and out the windows (× 3)
As you have done before.
Stand and face your partner (× 3)
As you have done before.

The grand old Duke of York
He had ten thousand men.
He marched them up to the top of the hill
And he marched them down again.
And when they were up, they were up
And when they were down, they were down
And when they were only half way up
They were neither up nor down.

Section 6

With your hands you clap, clap, clap,
With your foot you tap, tap, tap,
This foot first, that foot then
Round about and back again.
(The carer can add other movements:
With your arms you flap, flap, flap,
With your head you knack, knack, knack,
This foot first, that foot then
Round about and back again.)

Section 7

Humpty Dumpty sat on a wall
Humpty Dumpty had a great fall.
All the king's horses and all the king's men
Couldn't put Humpty together again.

Incy, wincy spider climbing up the spout,
Down came the rain and washed the spider out.
Out came the sun and dried up all the rain,
So incy wincy spider climbed the spout again.

APPENDIX II

Useful Addresses in the UK

The following lists are designed to guide. They are not comprehensive.

Therapy

Arts in Psychotherapy, Institute for
1 Beaconsfield Road
St Albans AL1 3RD

Arts Therapists, British Association of
11a Richmond Road
Brighton 2BN 3RL

Dance/Movement Therapists, the Association of
ADMT UK
c/o Quaker Meeting Rooms
Wedmore Vale
Bedminster
Bristol BS3 5JA

Drama Therapists, British Association of
The Old Mill
Tolpuddle
Dorchester
Dorset DT2 7XX

Nordoff Robins (Music Therapy)
2 Lissenden Gardens
Kentish Town
London NW5 1PQ

Osteopathic Clinic for Children
109 Harley Street
London W1N 1DG

Physiotherapy, the Chartered Society of
14 Bedford Row
London WC1R 4ED

Professional Music Therapists
c/o The Administrator
The Meadow
68 Pierce Lane
Fulbourn
Cambridge CB1 5DL

There are also groups which offer movement and music throughout the UK. Ask at your local information bureau.

Resources in the UK

Dance For Everyone
30 Sevington Road
London NW4 3RX
(videos giving examples of movements, and danced stories to stimulate creativity and literacy)

Early Learning Centre
(Branches in many High Streets)
Mail Order Dept
South Marsden Park
Swindon SN3 4TJ
(toys, games, books, equipment)

Music Education Suppliers
101 Banstead Road South
Sutton
Surrey SM2 5LH
(musical instruments)

Novara
Excelsior Road
Ashby Business Park
Ashby de la Zouch
LE65 1NG
(recreational activity equipment)

Portogram
212 High Street
Barnet
Herts EN5 5SZ
(variable speed tape recorders)

Rompa
Goyt Side Road
Chesterfield S40 2PH
(soft play)

Wicksteed Leisure Ltd
Digby Street
Kettering
Northants NN16 8YJ
(powder-coated metal structures)

BIBLIOGRAPHY

Axline VA, *Play Therapy*, Longmans, London, 1989.

Beard RM, *An Outline of Piaget's Developmental Psychology*, Routledge & Kegan Paul, London, 1969.

Benari N, *Inner Rhythm*, Harwood Academic Publishers, Chur, Switzerland, 1995.

Cohen E & Sekeles C, `Treatment of Down's Syndrome Children Through Music and Movement', *Fourth International Conference Papers*, DaCi, London, 1988.

Deutsch F, *On the Mysterious Leap from the Mind to the Body*, International Universities Press, New York, 1973.

Donaldson M, *Children's Minds*, Fontana Press, London, 1987.

Fraiberg S, `Intervention in Infancy: A Programme for Blind Infants', *Journal of the American Academy of Child Psychiatry*, 1971.

Freud S, *The Standard Edition of the Complete Psychological Works of Sigmund Freud, Vol XIX, `The Ego and the Id'*, Hogarth Press, London, 1923.

FunSongs Ltd, (ELT publisher: funsongs@patrol.i-way.co.uk).

Harrison K, *Look! Look What I Can Do!*, BBC Educational Publishing, London, 1996.

Leventhal MB, `Movement Therapy with Minimal Brain Dysfunction Children', *Focus on Dance VII: Dance Therapy*, National Dance Association, Reston, 1974.

Lewis Bernstein P, `Psychodynamic Ego Psychology in Developmental Dance–Movement Therapy', *Theoretical Approaches in Dance–Movement Therapy* I, Kendall Hunt, Dubuque, Iowa, 1986.

Meekums B, `Dance Movement Therapy and the Development of Mother–Child Interaction: a Pilot Study', *Fourth International Conference Papers*, DaCi, London, 1988.

Montagu A, *Touching*, Harper & Row Publishers, New York, 1978.

Payne H, *Creative Movement and Dance in Groupwork*, Winslow Press/Speechmark, Bicester, 1990.

Payne H (ed), *Dance Movement Therapy: Theory and Practice*, Routledge, London, 1992.

Pisciotta A, 'The Case for Dance for the Deaf', *Focus on Dance IX: Dance for the Handicapped,* National Dance Association, Reston, 1980.

Rayner E, *Human Development,* Unwin Hyman, London, 1971.

Rose B, 'Leap to Life: Dance Play and the Language Dysfunction Child', *Fourth International Conference Papers,* DaCi, London, 1988.

Schmais C, 'Observations on Dance Therapy as a Viable Treatment Modality for Visually Handicapped Individuals', *Focus on Dance VII: Dance Therapy,* National Dance Association, Reston, 1974.

Sherborne V, *Developmental Movement For Children,* Cambridge University Press, Cambridge, 1990.

Stern DN, *The Interpersonal World of the Infant,* Basic Books, New York, 1985.

Stern DN, *Diary of a Baby,* Fontana, London, 1991.

Taylor D, *Learning with Traditional Rhymes,* Ladybird Books Ltd, Loughborough, 1976.

Witkin RW, *The Intelligence of Feeling,* Heinemann Educational Books, London, 1974.